THE LADY OF BELMONT

BY THE SAME AUTHOR

NOVELS

> MRS. MARTIN'S MAN
> ALICE AND A FAMILY
> CHANGING WINDS
> THE FOOLISH LOVERS

SHORT STORIES

> EIGHT O'CLOCK AND OTHER
> STUDIES

PLAYS

> THE MAGNANIMOUS LOVER
> MIXED MARRIAGE
> JANE CLEGG
> JOHN FERGUSON
> THE SHIP
> MARY, MARY, QUITE CON-
> TRARY

POLITICAL STUDY

> SIR EDWARD CARSON AND
> THE ULSTER MOVEMENT

ESSAYS

> SOME IMPRESSIONS OF MY
> ELDERS

THE
LADY OF BELMONT

A PLAY IN FIVE ACTS

BY

ST. JOHN G. ERVINE

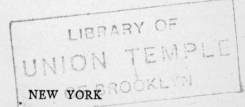

NEW YORK
THE MACMILLAN COMPANY
1924

Printed in Great Britain by
UNWIN BROTHERS, LIMITED, LONDON AND WOKING

TO

LAWRENCE LANGNER

THE FIRST ACT

A room, opening off a courtyard, in PORTIA's house in Belmont.
Early evening.

THE SECOND ACT

Same as Act I.   Two hours later.

THE THIRD ACT

A hall in PORTIA's house.   Three hours later.

THE FOURTH ACT

A bedroom in the house of LORENZO and JESSICA in Belmont.
Two hours later.

THE FIFTH ACT

The garden of PORTIA's house in Belmont.
The next morning.

The time is exactly ten years after the date of ANTONIO's
Trial in " The Merchant of Venice."

The entire action of the play takes place in less than twenty-
four hours.

CHARACTERS

PORTIA, a rich lady of Belmont, wife to BASSANIO.

NERISSA, formerly her maid, wife to GRATIANO.

JESSICA, SHYLOCK'S daughter and wife to LORENZO.

BASSANIO, a Venetian, living in Belmont.

ANTONIO, a retired merchant of Venice, living near BASSANIO.

DOCTOR BELLARIO, a lawyer of Padua and cousin to PORTIA.

GRATIANO
LORENZO
} Venetian friends of BASSANIO, living in Belmont.

YOUNG LORENZO, son to JESSICA and LORENZO.

LAUNCELOT GOBBO, LORENZO'S servant.

BALTHASAR, PORTIA'S steward.

STEPHANO, a young servant in PORTIA'S house.

SHYLOCK, a Jew of Venice.

A MESSENGER.

Servants, retainers, guests, etc.

THE FIRST ACT

The scene is laid in a room opening off a courtyard in PORTIA'S *house in Belmont. A short flight of steps lead from it to the rest of the house. People entering from the courtyard descend a flight of broad steps. A heavy gate, giving access to the courtyard from the public road, is visible.*

The time is the early evening. The scene steadily darkens during the action so that at the end of the first act the courtyard is dark, except for the illuminations.

[*Enter* BALTHASAR, PORTIA'S *Steward, a man of pompous manner, conceited and humourless. He is followed by* NERISSA, *now a matronly figure, but hardly so genial as she was in "The Merchant of Venice." Her face bears the signs of continual anxiety. Life with* GRATIANO *has not been so full of entertainment as she had hoped it would be. She is now in a state of anger, which is not made any less by the manner of* BALTHASAR.]

BALTHASAR. I will tell my mistress you are here, but I doubt if she will see you. She is busy, and has much to do.

NERISSA. Nevertheless, I wish to speak to her.

BALTHASAR. You know her cousin comes to-day?

NERISSA. Cousin! What cousin?

BALTHASAR. Doctor Bellario.

NERISSA. The lawyer?

BALTHASAR. From Padua. He has not been in this house for more than ten years.

NERISSA. Doctor Bellario! And is he friendly now to my lady?

BALTHASAR. I do not know whether he is friendly or not, but he is coming.

NERISSA (*cogitating*). H'm! I wonder what this means. Is it Bassanio who brings him here?

9

BALTHASAR. I am a discreet man, madam.

NERISSA. Come, come, Balthasar, your discretion is well enough for those who are strange to you, but I know you are as fond of gossip as any man on earth, especially if it be spiteful.

BALTHASAR. I have some of the failings of humanity, madam ! . . .

NERISSA. Well, then, tell me all. It *is* Bassanio that brings his lady's cousin here ? Eh ? Come, what's the trouble now ?

BALTHASAR. I will tell my lady you are here.

NERISSA. You were in no hurry to tell her when I first came, and my message can wait a little longer. Oh, Balthasar, I am hungry for a scandalous conversation. Gratify me. It *is* Bassanio, is it not ?

BALTHASAR. I fear my lady finds my lord importunate.

NERISSA. Importunate ! In love ?

BALTHASAR. Other ladies find him so, but his importunities to my mistress are not to her heart, but to her purse.

NERISSA. Indeed, I know. My husband ! . . .

BALTHASAR. Have you come here to complain of Gratiano ?

NERISSA. I have, God help me !

BALTHASAR. Then you may save your breath. My mistress is acquainted with your husband's habits, and does not like them. There is no spendthrift folly in which he and my lord Bassanio do not make a pair.

NERISSA. I'll thank you to leave my husband's habits to me, Balthasar. With all his faults, he is twice the man that you will ever be.

BALTHASAR. Perhaps, madam, the world does not share your opinion.

NERISSA. Your satisfaction with yourself, Balthasar, makes me feel exceedingly sick.

BALTHASAR. Better be sick, madam, with self-satisfaction than be sick, as you are, with disappointment. Here comes Antonio.

NERISSA. Don't leave me with him ! He'll tell me again how near he was to losing his pound of flesh !

[*She turns to fly from the room, but* ANTONIO *enters from the courtyard before she has time to do so.*]

ANTONIO. Ah, my gentle Nerissa!

[ANTONIO *has aged considerably in the last ten years. He has a fretful, misunderstood manner, and his priggishness and pomposity are now lacking in the dignity which enabled him to carry off his grand signior ways in Venice.*]

NERISSA. Good-day to you, Antonio, sir.

ANTONIO. I have not seen you—how long?

NERISSA. A week. That's all. A short week.

ANTONIO. I am sure it is longer ago than that . . .

NERISSA. Only a week, Antonio. (*To* BALTHASAR.) I pray you, tell my lady I am here.

[BALTHASAR *goes into the house.*

ANTONIO. We are getting old, Nerissa, very old.

NERISSA. I do not feel myself so old.

ANTONIO. Oh, but you are, and getting older. One of these mornings, Nerissa, you will see your face in the glass, and you will know that you are old, very old. And some of your friends will say you should have discovered it long ago.

NERISSA. You are a comfortable companion, Antonio!

ANTONIO. I do not flatter. Why should I? No one flatters me. Do you know what day this is, Nerissa?

NERISSA. Yes! Wednesday!

ANTONIO. I do not mean a common, ordinary sort of a Wednesday. Think, Nerissa!

NERISSA. Why should one Wednesday be more than any other Wednesday? They are all Wednesdays to me.

ANTONIO. What a fickle thing is the memory of man! Why, Nerissa, on this day, ten years ago, my life was sought! . . .

NERISSA. I know the story well. I have heard it before.

ANTONIO. By Shylock, there in Venice. A Jew! God save us all, a Jew!

NERISSA. I wonder if it will rain to-night.

ANTONIO. Rain! Why should it rain?

NERISSA. I do not know. I wondered.

ANTONIO. You put me off my argument with your irrelevant speculations on weather. This Jew, Shylock, had a bond of me that I should lose a pound of flesh—flesh, mark you !—to be cut off by him nearest my heart if I should fail to pay him some three thousand ducats that he had lent Bassanio on my security.

NERISSA. Indeed, Antonio, I know the story only too well.

ANTONIO. A pound of flesh ! Nearest my heart ! Here ! This very spot ! I'll show it to you !

> [*He begins to unfasten his doublet.*

NERISSA. I beg you, no ! I have seen it many times before, and I have a nervous heart.

ANTONIO (*doing his doublet up again*). Well, then, you shall not see it. Do you think, Nerissa, I should have died if Shylock had had his bond ?

NERISSA. Perhaps ! One never knows !

ANTONIO. They tell me surgeons have great skill with flesh, and can undo a man and tie him up again and leave him better than he was. Some say we have too many organs inside us.

NERISSA. I can well believe it !

ANTONIO. I might have lived.

NERISSA. Oh, no doubt of that !

ANTONIO. I fear sometimes Bassanio does not remember how much he owes me. He is very careless with his friends.

NERISSA. Aye, and with his wife and her fortune.

ANTONIO. But not to remember his debt to me ; that's ingratitude, Nerissa, gross ingratitude. A man may fail in circumspection to his wife and not be chid for it, but to fail his friend—and such a friend !—no, no, that's ingratitude ! I nearly lost my life for him.

NERISSA. And it was saved by Portia.

ANTONIO. Yes, yes, of course, and I am grateful to her.

> [*Re-enter* BALTHASAR. *As he does so,* LORENZO *comes into the courtyard.*]

BALTHASAR. My lady bids me bring you to her chamber.

NERISSA. I'll go at once. (*Enter* LORENZO.) Why Lorenzo, I thought you were gone to France.

LORENZO. I am on my way, but have stopped to take leave of Portia. Good evening, Antonio !

ANTONIO. Good evening, good evening!

LORENZO (*to* BALTHASAR). Is she within?

BALTHASAR. She is, my lord. I'll tell her you are here.

NERISSA. There is no need. I'll take you to her room, Lorenzo. This house is my familiar ground.

BALTHASAR. I do not think my lady! . . .

NERISSA. Tush, Balthasar, you are far too formal! Come, Lorenzo, I have something to say to you about your wife.

LORENZO. My wife! Jessica?

NERISSA. I've heard Bassanio's roving eye has lit on her! . . .

LORENZO. Nerissa!

NERISSA. Come! I'll tell you more!

[*They go out together,* LORENZO *expostulating.*

ANTONIO (*to* BALTHASAR). Did you tell your mistress I was here?

BALTHASAR. I did not, my lord.

ANTONIO. Then you are a fool, and do not know your office.

BALTHASAR. A fool, my lord?

ANTONIO. An ass! A jackass! . . .

BALTHASAR. My lord!

[*Enter* LAUNCELOT GOBBO, *from the courtyard in a furtive manner.* GOBBO *has grown slyer in his ways and is a little less certain of himself than he was ten years ago, but he is still something of an amusing rogue.*]

ANTONIO (*to* BALTHASAR). Go now, and tell her I am here.

BALTHASAR. One moment, sir. (*To* GOBBO.) Well, fellow, what is your business?

GOBBO. I wish to see lord Bassanio.

BALTHASAR. He is not at home.

GOBBO. Will it be long before he returns?

BALTHASAR. I do not know.

GOBBO. Then I'll wait. My business is important.

BALTHASAR. As you please. (*To* ANTONIO.) I will acquaint my lady with your presence, sir. (*He mounts the short flight of steps. Then he turns and speaks to* GOBBO.) Your master, Lorenzo, is here.

GOBBO (*dismayed*). My master! . . .

BALTHASAR. I will tell him you are waiting.

GOBBO. No, no, Balthasar, I pray you. My matter is not for his ears.

BALTHASAR. Oh! For whose ears may it be?

GOBBO (*slyly*). Your master's.

BALTHASAR (*understandingly*). I see. Very well! (*Exit.*)

GOBBO (*aside*). That's a pompous ass. He eats starch for dinner and dreams of ramrods.

ANTONIO. Here, fellow!

GOBBO. Sir!

ANTONIO. You are a Venetian?

GOBBO. I am, and you know me well, sir, though your memory is defective. My name is Gobbo, Launcelot Gobbo. I was servant in Venice to Shylock that took a liking to your worship's flesh! . . .

ANTONIO. Servant to Shylock, were you?

GOBBO. And afterwards to my lord Bassanio here, and would be servant to him still, but that my lady could not bear the sight of me. Now I serve Lorenzo that married the Jew's daughter, Jessica.

ANTONIO. I thought I knew your face, but could not remember where I had seen you. Have you ever been in prison?

GOBBO. No, sir, not yet.

ANTONIO. Then you are lucky. But be warned, your luck will not last for ever. You have a most villainous appearance, and on your face alone are certain to be hanged.

GOBBO. Do you wish to say anything more to me, sir?

ANTONIO. Yes. Do you know what day this is?

GOBBO. I am not rightly certain, sir. I slept the clock round on Saturday, and have not yet caught up with time, but some say 'tis Wednesday, though I would not swear to it.

ANTONIO. They all say 'tis Wednesday, as if it were any Wednesday. Why, fellow, 'twas this day, ten years ago, my life was sought by that Jew you served in Venice, that moneylender, Shylock.

GOBBO. Was it, sir?

ANTONIO. But no one remembers, except myself.

GOBBO. We should have remembered the day better, sir, if the Jew had got your flesh. 'Twas always the way of men, sir, to remember successful villainy longer than successful virtue. Here comes my lord Bassanio, and Gratiano with him.

[*Enter* BASSANIO *from the courtyard, followed by* GRATIANO. BASSANIO *is stouter and coarser and more assured in his manner than he was when he came wooing* PORTIA. GRATIANO *has not got so much assurance as* BASSANIO, *but he resembles him otherwise.*]

BASSANIO. Why, here's old Antonio!

ANTONIO. My dear Bassanio! And you, Gratiano!

BASSANIO. What brings you here?

ANTONIO. The hope of seeing you. I am always glad to see you, Bassanio.

GOBBO (*plucking at* BASSANIO'S *sleeve*). My lord!

ANTONIO. Remembering what took place ten years ago this very day, I resolved that I would come and celebrate its memory with you and Portia.

BASSANIO. Oh! And what took place ten years ago?

ANTONIO. What took place! Merciful Father! . . .

BASSANIO. I know! Portia and I were wed!

GRATIANO. And so were Nerissa and I. But is that a cause for celebration, Antonio?

ANTONIO. No, no, I am not talking of your wedding-day, but the day of my deliverance from the Jew.

BASSANIO. Oh, that! Do you hear, Gratiano, it is ten years ago since poor old Antonio nearly lost his pound of flesh.

GRATIANO. I did not think it was so long, and yet sometimes it seems longer.

ANTONIO. I thought the Duke of Venice would have sent a friendly word to me, but no, no one remembers! And when I come here to celebrate the day, I find the house prepared to greet another guest.

BASSANIO. Another guest!

ANTONIO. Yes. Doctor Bellario!

BASSANIO. Doctor Bellario! By heaven, I had forgotten him. Is he here yet?

ANTONIO. No, not yet.

BASSANIO. That's luck! Oh, Gratiano, I'm in fortune. If I had stayed as you begged me to, Portia would never have forgiven me.

ANTONIO. However, this festival for your cousin will serve also as a festival for me.

GOBBO (*again plucking at* BASSANIO's *sleeve*). My lord!

BASSANIO. What, fellow! Oh, Gobbo, what do you want?

GOBBO. I have a private message for you, my lord.

BASSANIO. From whom?

GOBBO. The lady Jessica!

BASSANIO. Hush!

[*Enter* BALTHASAR.

BALTHASAR. My mistress comes, my lord.

[GOBBO *hides himself. Enter* PORTIA, *followed by* NERISSA *and* LORENZO. BASSANIO *goes to her and kisses her hand.* NERISSA *joins* GRATIANO, *and talks to him in terms of remonstrance.*]

PORTIA. I was afraid you would be too late to greet my cousin.

BASSANIO. That was foolish of you. I am as eager to welcome him as you, my dear.

PORTIA. Here's Lorenzo come to take his leave.

BASSANIO. Why, Lorenzo, where are you bound for?

LORENZO. For France. I have business that takes me there, and now that I have seen you both, I'll continue my journey.

PORTIA. A swift and fair return, Lorenzo.

LORENZO. Thank you, Portia. (*He kisses her hand.*) Good-bye, Bassanio.

BASSANIO. Good-bye, Lorenzo. We must see more of each other when you come back.

NERISSA (*aside to* GRATIANO). He would do better to see less of Jessica while Lorenzo's gone.

GRATIANO. Hold your silly tongue!

LORENZO. Good-bye! Good-bye!

[*General farewells.*

NERISSA. Good-bye, Lorenzo. (*Quietly.*) If you are wise you'll not go far to-night. Sleep at the Venetian's tavern, outside the town.

LORENZO. I do not like this plotting! . . .

NERISSA (*aloud*). Good-bye, and safe return from France.

[*Exit* LORENZO.

PORTIA. Well, dear Antonio! Nerissa says that you have come to make a celebration, too.

ANTONIO. I have, and with your leave, dear Portia, I'll share your festival with Doctor Bellario.

PORTIA. Do. This is a day of great happiness for me. My cousin was not pleased with me for what I did when I defended you from the Jew.

ANTONIO. Not pleased! Did he, then, wish me dead?

PORTIA. Not dead, but better defended. 'Tis a long story, Antonio, and I will not tire your ears with it, but, briefly, he was out of friends with me because I took his place before the Duke of Venice.

ANTONIO. But you brought a letter from him, commending you to the Duke.

PORTIA. I did, and wrote it, too!

ANTONIO. Wrote it! I do not understand your meaning.

PORTIA. 'Tis plain enough. My cousin, being ill, bade me carry a letter to the Duke, expounding the law to him, but when I read it, I bethought me of a scheme to tease my husband here, and so I wrote another letter, as like my cousin's writing as I could, and putting on his robes, set forth for Venice, where I played the lawyer's part and set you free. My cousin, when he heard what I had done, was very angry, and swore he would not speak to me again.

ANTONIO. But why?

PORTIA. Because I had made for the young lawyer all the reputation he had hoped to make for himself. I am sorry now. It is not pleasant for an old man to be cheated out of his reputation. But he has forgiven me, and to-day he comes to stay a while in my house.

BASSANIO. His decision was quickly made. What did you say to him?

PORTIA. I doubt if you would care to hear.

BASSANIO. Then it was about me?

PORTIA. We will not discuss our affairs now, Bassanio. The time for that will come soon enough. Nerissa, here, complains that you take her lord too often away from her.

BASSANIO. I do not take him! . . .

GRATIANO. No, indeed, you don't. I go of my own free will. I thank God I have a mind and can make it up.

NERISSA. Well, then, my lord, make up your mind to this. I like not loneliness. Where have you been these five days and nights?

GRATIANO. Can a man not go hunting without having to tell his wife all he does? There's a plague of tiresome women that will have a man detail his life for them, with a " What did you say to him? " and " What did he say to you? " and " Where were you at such an hour? " as if he had memory of all he did. Bassanio and I went hunting. That's enough for you!

NERISSA. Hunting what?

GRATIANO. Hunting, my dear, just hunting!

PORTIA. Bassanio, I have not asked you much of late, but now I must beg you to curb your pleasure. It has cost me dear, and my fortune will not bear much more. My cousin will confer with me on how to meet our debts.

BASSANIO. So that is why your cousin comes! It is no friendly visit, but an inquisition. Had I known this, I should have taken my time in hurrying home to greet him.

PORTIA. When he arrives, Bassanio, if you are not here to welcome him, my pardon will be hard to find. Balthasar, are all the invitations sent?

BALTHASAR. They are, my gracious lady.

[*While* PORTIA *is talking to* BALTHASAR, GOBBO *sidles from his hiding-place and speaks to* BASSANIO.]

PORTIA. There must be many coloured lights when my cousin comes! And music!

BALTHASAR. It shall be as you wish, my lady. At what hour does Dr. Bellario arrive?

PORTIA. Soon after dark. Why is Gobbo here?

BALTHASAR. I do not know, my lady. He brought a message for my lord.

PORTIA. From whom?

BALTHASAR. He did not say.

PORTIA. Bid him begone.

[BALTHASAR *leaves her and is seen speaking to* GOBBO, *whom he compels to leave the room.* GOBBO *goes into the courtyard, where he conceals himself.*]

PORTIA. Let us go in. All of you will dine to-night

with my cousin and us. Balthasar, while we are within, bid the servants light the lamps. I wish the house to look gay when Doctor Bellario arrives.

BALTHASAR. As you please, my lady.

[*Exit* BALTHASAR.

PORTIA. Antonio!

ANTONIO. I come, my dear.

PORTIA. You'll follow me, Nerissa, with my husband and your lord.

[*She goes into the house with* ANTONIO.

GRATIANO. Now, look here, Nerissa, understand once and for all, that I will not have you wagging your tongue about me to Portia.

NERISSA. I'll wag it as I please, and to whom I please.

BASSANIO. If I were your lord, you'd wag it circumspectly, madam.

NERISSA. If I were your wife, Bassanio, I'd wag it to some purpose.

BASSANIO. What do you mean?

NERISSA (*half-way up the steps*). Ask the little Jewess, Jessica.

BASSANIO. Hell, woman! . . . (*But she has flown.*) Gratiano, you must make her hold her tongue.

GRATIANO. I will, if you will tell me how!

BASSANIO. Let's follow them.

[GOBBO *returns.*

GOBBO. My lord!

BASSANIO. What! (*Then, seeing who it is.*) Go before me, Gratiano, and say I'll follow in a little while.

GRATIANO. I'll make a good excuse for you. (*Exit.*)

BASSANIO. What is it, Gobbo?

GOBBO. I have a message for you from my mistress.

BASSANIO. What is it?

GOBBO. She bade me say that my lord Lorenzo's gone to France. She is alone.

BASSANIO. Oh!

GOBBO. If you will please to come to her! . . .

BASSANIO. Tell her I cannot come. My lady's cousin, Doctor Bellario, arrives to-night, and I must stay to welcome him.

GOBBO. My mistress is alone, my lord.

BASSANIO. So you said before.

GOBBO. And loves you, my lord!

BASSANIO (*catching him by the throat*). Damned cur, what's that to you?

GOBBO (*on his knees*). My lord, I speak but for your pleasure. (BASSANIO *releases him*.) I get a poor reward for my labours in your service.

BASSANIO. Stop this snivelling! . . .

GOBBO. Yes, my lord! I'll go now.

> [*He moves towards the courtyard.*

BASSANIO. Come back. (GOBBO *returns*.) Well?

GOBBO. She sits and waits for you, my lord, and sighs and sobs because you will not come to her.

BASSANIO. Tell her perhaps I'll come to-morrow.

GOBBO. She hopes you'll come now.

BASSANIO. Now! I've told you, cur, my lady's cousin! . . .

GOBBO. Has not yet arrived, my lord, and will not come 'til it be dark. I heard my lady say the same herself.

> [*Enter BALTHASAR, followed by servants with lights.*

BALTHASAR. Come, come, you clowns. Light the lamps and set the festival!

BASSANIO. What's this, Balthasar?

BALTHASAR. My lady bade me light the lamps at once, my lord. (*To the servants*.) Come, bustle, clowns, or dawn will be here before you've done.

> [*Other servants appear in the courtyard, and gradually the darkening scene is lit by many coloured lamps. The servants leave as they finish. They have all gone when GOBBO goes.*]

GOBBO. My lord!

BASSANIO. Are you still here?

GOBBO. If you will see my mistress now, you can be back again before the doctor comes. He will not be here for two hours and more. Shall I tell her you will come?

BASSANIO. No.

GOBBO. Her face is lovely in the dusk, my lord, and she adores you.

BALTHASAR (*in the courtyard*). Come, come, dogs, more light, more light! (*He strikes a servant with his staff.*)

BASSANIO. Where did you learn to speak so enticingly?

GOBBO.   I listened while you made love, my lord!

BASSANIO.   Rascal!

GOBBO.   I've found you a good preceptor, sir.   Many a wench have I conquered with words I learned from you. Long, languishing words, my lord, that make a woman's heart ache with desire!   I learnt them all from you! There was a cook in Belmont once that had the lightest hand I ever knew in making cakes and pies, but she was hard to court until I told her words I'd heard you say, and then she was easy!   Her husband, a slow, sluggardly fellow, could not prove the child was mine! . . .

BASSANIO.   Gobbo, you are a villain!

GOBBO.   'Tis true, my lord, and since I'm damned beyond redemption, I'll get what paradise I can while I'm alive.   Will you come, my lord?   (BASSANIO *considers this appeal, but does not reply to it.*)   She is an amorous woman, and makes no more demand of you than this, that you'll be kind to her.

BASSANIO.   I'll go to her.   (BALTHASAR *enters from the courtyard.*)   Balthasar, if your mistress should inquire for me, tell her I have gone along the road to meet her cousin, Doctor Bellario.

BALTHASAR.   I will, my lord.

[*Exit* BASSANIO *through the courtyard.*

BALTHASAR.   Well, why do you not go?

GOBBO.   Because I wish to gaze upon you, Balthasar, and marvel at the works of God.

BALTHASAR.   I do not require your approval, my good Gobbo.

GOBBO.   Your good Gobbo, indeed!   I'll good Gobbo you, you gobbling cock-sparrow!   Mend your manners, master ninepence, and learn to recognize and respect a man that, though he may not have your fortune, deserves it better.   Your good Gobbo, indeed!   I should have your office still had I been more circumspect with women!

BALTHASAR.   I cannot spare time for argument with you, Gobbo.   You have a loose disposition, and I am notoriously a chaste man.   Hence the difference in our fortunes.

GOBBO.   You will surely go to heaven when you die,

for God knows you are unlikely to cause confusion among the holy angels.

BALTHASAR. Begone! My mistress comes.

[*Exit* GOBBO. *Enter* PORTIA.

PORTIA. Where is your lord, Balthasar?

BALTHASAR. He bade me tell you, my lady, that he had gone to meet your cousin, Doctor Bellario.

PORTIA. Gone to meet my cousin! Are you sure he said that?

BALTHASAR. I am, my lady. His words precisely were " If your mistress should inquire for me, tell her I have gone along the road to meet her cousin, Doctor Bellario." I noted them in my mind at the time.

PORTIA. I am very glad. Was not that Launcelot Gobbo who stole away just now?

BALTHASAR. It was, my lady! A low, ribald fellow, my lady, full of envy and evil wishes. (*He turns to go.*)

PORTIA. One moment, Balthasar!

BALTHASAR. My lady!

PORTIA. This Gobbo, whose servant is he now?

BALTHASAR. I am not well acquainted with the lives of the lower servants, my lady, but I have heard he serves with lord Lorenzo.

PORTIA. Lorenzo!

BALTHASAR. He once was servant, so 'tis said, to lord Lorenzo's father, the Jew of Venice.

PORTIA. Yes! How brightly you have lit the house, Balthasar!

BALTHASAR. My lady, in all I do, I strive to be worthy of your commendation. May I withdraw?

PORTIA. Send Stephano to me.

BALTHASAR. He's by, my lady. I'll summon him. (*He goes to the entrance to the courtyard and calls.*) Stephano!

STEPHANO (*off*). Hola! Hola!

BALTHASAR. He comes, my lady!

PORTIA. Do you like music, Balthasar?

BALTHASAR. I can listen to it, my lady.

PORTIA. Young lord Lorenzo loves music. I remember when he first came here with Jessica, his bride! . . . Jessica! . . .

BALTHASAR. Yes, my lady!

PORTIA (*rousing herself*).   I was dreaming, Balthasar, of young times long ago.   But not so long ago, not so long in years as long in thought.   Lord Lorenzo would sing and play to Jessica ! . . . How I think on Jessica to-night !

[*Enter* STEPHANO.

BALTHASAR.   Stephano is here, my lady.

PORTIA.   Ah, Stephano !

STEPHANO.   My lady !

PORTIA.   Sing that song to me which I taught you for the festival.   Balthasar, you must stay and hear it, too.

BALTHASAR.   My lady, I am no musician.

PORTIA.   Nevertheless, I wish you to hear my song. Sing, Stephano.

STEPHANO *sings.*

Come, master youth, count up your charity,
If that your love be not all you desire.
Have you not heard that perfection's a rarity ?
Wedding, like wooing, 's a flickering fire.
Then droop not,
Then stoop not,
Never repine,
Love's a dream that won't come true,
Take what life shall bring to you,
And make it do.

[*As the song ends, a violent knocking is heard on the gate
in the courtyard.*]

PORTIA.   What noise is that ?

BALTHASAR.   Someone knocks on the gate, my lady ! I will see who it is.

[BALTHASAR *goes into the courtyard and opens the gate.
He speaks to the messenger whom he finds there.*]

PORTIA.   You have sung well, Stephano, and I will reward you.

STEPHANO.   Shall I continue, my lady?

PORTIA.   Not now, Stephano !

[BALTHASAR *returns.*

BALTHASAR.   My lady, a messenger has come from Doctor Bellario.

PORTIA.   From Doctor Bellario ! Bid him enter.

[BALTHASAR *beckons to the messenger, who enters and
kneels before* PORTIA.]

PORTIA.   Are you from Doctor Bellario?

MESSENGER.   I am, my lady. He bids me tell you that he is almost here, two hours before his time. We travelled faster than we thought.

PORTIA.   Balthasar, see that my servants are prepared. Warn all the house that my cousin's come. (*To the* MESSENGER, *as* BALTHASAR *goes out.*) Did my lord Bassanio send a message with you?

MESSENGER.   Lord Bassanio?

PORTIA.   Yes. Did he not send a message, too?

MESSENGER.   I have not seen my lord Bassanio.

PORTIA.   Was he not with your master when you left?

MESSENGER.   No, my lady.

[*Enter* BALTHASAR *from the courtyard, where servants are now seen, increasingly busy with their preparations for* BELLARIO'S *reception.*]

PORTIA.   Balthasar!

BALTHASAR.   My lady!

PORTIA.   Did you not say my lord had gone to meet Doctor Bellario?

BALTHASAR.   He bade me say so, my lady!

PORTIA.   Very well! See that this messenger is well attended.   I'll go and make ready for my cousin's coming! (*She mounts the steps leading into the house and pauses on the top one.*) That *was* Gobbo, was it not, that loitered here a while ago?

BALTHASAR.   It was, my lady. An ill-conditioned fellow! . . .

PORTIA.   Yes.   (*She pauses for a moment as if in thought, then she goes out.*)

BALTHASAR.   Is your master far from Belmont?

MESSENGER.   No. He may be here at any hour.

BALTHASAR.   I'll summon a servant to make you comfortable. (*At the outer courtyard.*) Hola, there! One of you! (*To the* MESSENGER.) You must be gratified at finding yourself among noble people. Have you ever been in Belmont before?

MESSENGER.   No.

BALTHASAR.   It is a great privilege.

[*Enter a* SERVANT *from the outer courtyard.*

MESSENGER.   We have some nobility in Padua.

BALTHASAR. Possibly. (*To the* SERVANT.) See that this visitor is made comfortable within, and warn your fellows that Doctor Bellario may arrive at any moment.

[*The* SERVANT, *accompanied by the* MESSENGER, *goes out by the courtyard.*]

STEPHANO. What do you think, Master Balthasar, of my lady's song?

BALTHASAR. It is a dingy piece, but it has an agreeable moral.

STEPHANO. It's very sad.

BALTHASAR. That is why the moral is so agreeable. You are young, Stephano, and inclined to entertain romantic thoughts. When you are twice your age, my boy, you will be thankful if things are no worse than you expect them to be.

STEPHANO. Oh, master Balthasar, you *are* a melancholy man.

BALTHASAR. Not melancholy, Stephano. Experienced. I am in a mood to moralize, my boy. Stay by me for a moment!

STEPHANO. But is there time?

BALTHASAR. Abundance. All my preparations are made. Let me warn you against romantic thoughts, Stephano. I have been held in high esteem by wise and well-placed men because I have never permitted a romantic thought to interrupt my career. Not, mark you, that I have never been visited by romantic thoughts. I have. Often. But whenever such a thought came to me and seemed likely to disturb my life, I said to myself, " This is emotional! " and I brushed it aside. The result is that I have won confidence and trust from great people which would never have been given to any romantic person.

STEPHANO. Have you never loved a woman, master Balthasar?

BALTHASAR. I have, on several occasions, but always with discretion.

STEPHANO. But haven't you ever had an overpowering love for a woman?

BALTHASAR. I thank God, Stephano, that I have never been overpowered by anything in my life. I admire women very much, but I do not permit myself to be excessive about them.

STEPHANO. I would love to feel a fierce and uncontrollable passion for a woman.

BALTHASAR. My advice to any young man is this: Be temperate in all things, but especially in love. When you press a woman to your heart, Stephano, do so discreetly and in a moderate manner, so that she may know you are still capable of resisting her. Your father, God rest his soul, was an immoderate man. With what result? He is a corpse and you are an orphan.

STEPHANO. But do not moderate men die also, master Balthasar?

BALTHASAR. They do, but not so precipitately.

[*Enter a* SERVANT *in haste.*

BALTHASAR. How now, rascal?

SERVANT. Oh, master Balthasar, the guest is come.

BALTHASAR. Already!

SERVANT. He is almost at the gate.

BALTHASAR. Summon all the servants to the courtyard to bid him welcome. Stir, stir! (*The* SERVANT *goes out.*) Go, Stephano, and tell my lady her cousin has arrived.

[*Exit* STEPHANO. SERVANTS *appear in the courtyard, which becomes once more full of activity.*]

Be busy, louts and rascals, and when the learned lawyer comes, cheer as if you were glad to see him. (*He goes towards the gates, which have been opened wide by the servants.*) Welcome, welcome, good Doctor Bellario! . . .

[PORTIA'S *servants make loud sounds of welcome, and some of* BELLARIO'S *servants enter, carrying torches, and are greeted noisily. A trumpet sounds.* PORTIA, *very beautifully dressed, enters from the house and goes to the opening on to the outer courtyard. The hubbub increases in volume. There is music and singing and a great display of coloured lights and torches. Then a passage is made in the crowd, and* DOCTOR BELLARIO *appears. He is an elderly, cynical-looking man.* PORTIA *goes to greet him. He takes her in his arms and kisses her affectionately. Then they both come into the house from the courtyard.*]

PORTIA. My dear cousin, I am glad to bid you welcome again to my house.

BELLARIO. You are not more glad to see me here, Portia, than I am to come. I love this house and often came to it while your father was alive ! . . .

PORTIA. It is a grief to me that you have not been here since my marriage.

BELLARIO. Well, well, we'll say no more of that. I lost heavily in reputation through your act, my dear, but we'll say no more of it.

PORTIA. That's more than kind, cousin.

BELLARIO. The whole world would have known my name through that case, had you not misbehaved.

[*The hubbub in the outer courtyard dies down, and the curtains separating the outer from the inner court-yard are drawn.*]

PORTIA. I am sorry for it, dear cousin !

BELLARIO. Well, well, we'll say no more about it. But when I think of how my judgment in that case would have sealed me with the world's renown, O, Portia, Portia !

PORTIA. I can never recompense you, cousin.

BELLARIO. No, you can't—but we'll say no more about it. Where is your husband ?

PORTIA. He went to meet you on the road.

BELLARIO. Then he missed me. Which is odd, for there is only one road.

PORTIA. He will be here presently.

[ANTONIO *enters.*

PORTIA (*taking* ANTONIO *by the hand and leading him to* BELLARIO.) Here is one, dear cousin, of more than common interest to you

BELLARIO. Is he in trouble with the law ?

PORTIA. Not now, but was. This is Antonio.

BELLARIO. Antonio !

ANTONIO. I am the merchant of Venice ! . . .

BELLARIO. There are many merchants in Venice, sir.

ANTONIO. But none with my reputation.

PORTIA. Antonio is the merchant whose life was sought in Venice by the Jew.

BELLARIO. Oh, yes, yes, yes! I remember now, of course. My cousin and I were just this moment talking of your case, sir. You were the defendant, were you not?

ANTONIO. I was.

BELLARIO. Yes. Yes, yes! It was on your account I quarrelled with my cousin here. Sir, you recall bitter memories to me.

ANTONIO. I myself have bitter memories, sir. Do you know that Shylock as nearly got a pound of my flesh as makes no difference?

BELLARIO. Portia, every time I look on him, I shall think of the wrong you did me.

PORTIA. I trust not, cousin.

ANTONIO. I begin to believe that I am not really popular! . . .

PORTIA. Oh, my dear Antonio, how can you say so?

ANTONIO. Look how everyone regards me! I'm an old man, but I have enough wit left to see that my friends are not effusive about me.

PORTIA. We love you, dear Antonio! . . .

ANTONIO. You say so, and perhaps *you* do, Portia, but Bassanio, whom I loved like my son, dissembles amazingly well. When I came here an hour ago, and told him that this day ten years I was in danger of my death for him, he scarcely had remembrance of it.

PORTIA. He teased you, Antonio.

ANTONIO. And now your cousin here says the sight of me will fill him with bitter memories. I had best go home.

PORTIA. Nay, you shall not. You'll stay and join our festival. Come, cousin, come within and refresh yourself. You'll find Nerissa, that was my clerk, at dinner here to-night. She'll give you deep instruction in the law. I have arranged a feast for you, and there'll be dancing and a youth who sings. Come, Antonio!

BELLARIO. I shall be glad to rest and refresh myself, for I have travelled far to-day.

PORTIA. Come, Antonio!

ANTONIO. Not now. I'll go to my own house, and in the evening when the feast is on, perhaps I'll come again. I bid you good-evening, Doctor Bellario!

BELLARIO. Good evening, sir, to you. (ANTONIO *goes into the courtyard.*)

PORTIA (*calling after him*). Good evening, then, my dear Antonio, but come again to-night.

ANTONIO. I'll think on it, Portia. (*Exit.*)

BELLARIO. That old gentleman is tedious. He is like all litigants. He harps too much on one note.

PORTIA. That is a common way of playing, cousin. I've heard many harp that way.

BELLARIO. True. We all do it. Even I, who am a well-balanced man, sometimes repeat myself.

PORTIA. I am sorry for Antonio. He has nothing in his mind now but his faded reputation, and he does not bear diminishment with dignity. Which of us does? When I am as old as old Antonio, I shall probably find the young impatient with my tales of vanished greatness.

BELLARIO. The remedy for that, my dear Portia, is not to let your greatness vanish.

PORTIA. But there's an enemy we cannot conquer, cousin, our ancient enemy, the clock.

[*Enter* BALTHASAR *from the courtyard.*

BALTHASAR. My lady!

PORTIA. Yes, Balthasar?

BALTHASAR. There is an old man, richly dressed, who's fainted by your gate.

PORTIA. Is it Antonio? He left us a moment since.

BALTHASAR. No, my lady, I do not know this man. He must be a great person in his own country, for I think he is a foreigner.

PORTIA. Bring him in.

[BALTHASAR *goes out.*

BELLARIO. This is some trick of Antonio's to win sympathy. Old men are cunning at such tricks.

PORTIA. But Balthasar says it is not Antonio.

[BALTHASAR *pulls the curtains aside, and two* SERVANTS *enter, carrying a richly dressed old man.*]

BALTHASAR. This is the man, my lady!

PORTIA. Do you not know him?

BALTHASAR. I have never seen him before. He is not a man of Belmont.

PORTIA.   Take him to another room and be kind to him.
He is old and looks very tired.   (*The* SERVANTS *prepare to
carry the old man away, but as they do so he stirs and recovers.*)
One moment.   He recovers.   Lay him down gently.

SHYLOCK (*for it is he.*)   Give me water!

BALTHASAR.   He desires a drink of water, my lady.

PORTIA.   One of you bring him some wine.

[BALTHASAR *instructs a servant to do so.*

SHYLOCK.   What place is this?

BALTHASAR.   This is the palace of my lady.   You are
in Belmont.

SHYLOCK.   In Belmont.   Yes, I remember now.   Is
that your lady?

BALTHASAR.   Madam, he desires to speak to you.

SHYLOCK.   I thank you, madam, for your kindness and
hospitality to a stranger.   I fear I have discomposed
your house by my unseasonable sickness.

PORTIA.   Rest here awhile, sir, until you are well again.

SHYLOCK.   Thank you!   It was a faintness that overtook
me on the road.

PORTIA.   You are welcome, sir, to all my house can
give you.

SHYLOCK.   That is great kindness, madam.   (*Peering at
her.*)   Have I not seen you in some other place?

PORTIA.   I do not know.   If you come often to
Belmont! . . .

SHYLOCK.   I have never been in Belmont before.   Yet I
remember to have seen someone like you.

PORTIA.   Where was it that you saw me?

SHYLOCK.   If I could remember that, madam, I could
remember you.   What is your name?

PORTIA.   My name is Portia.   Do you know it?

SHYLOCK.   No. I have never heard it before.   But I
have seen your face or someone who resembled you.   Have
you a brother?

PORTIA.   No, nor sister neither.

SHYLOCK.   It is a fancy.

PORTIA.   My servants will conduct you to a room where
you may rest and recover.   Balthasar!

BALTHASAR.   Yes, my lady?

[*He leads* SHYLOCK *towards the steps going into the house.*

PORTIA.   What is your name, sir?

SHYLOCK (*pausing and turning to her*).   Shylock!

PORTIA (*startled*).   Shylock!

SHYLOCK.   Shylock is my name!

BALTHASAR.   This way, sir!

      [BALTHASAR *goes out, followed by* SHYLOCK.

BELLARIO.   What's his name?

PORTIA.   Shylock!

BELLARIO.   Shylock! Was not that the name of the Jew who sought Antonio's life?

PORTIA.   It was.

BELLARIO.   Sola! sola! By our lady this will be a feast of fun, indeed!

      [*They go into the house and the curtain falls.*

THE SECOND ACT

*The scene is the same as that of the first act. The time is
two hours later. The curtains which separate the outer
from the inner courtyard are now drawn, but when
they are opened for any purpose, the audience catches
glimpses of bright lights.*

> [BALTHASAR *descends the steps leading from the house and
> goes through the curtains into the outer courtyard.
> In a moment or two, he returns, accompanied by*
> ANTONIO. *Both of them are wearing gayer clothes
> than they wore in the first act.*]

BALTHASAR. So your worship has decided to attend the
feast ?

ANTONIO. Yes, Balthasar. I thought it would look
strange if I were not present. A slight from me, however
slight ! . . . Ha, ha, ha, Balthasar, I can still jest, you see !

BALTHASAR (*who has not seen the joke*). Jest, your
worship !

ANTONIO. Yes, Balthasar. A slight from me, however
slight ! . . . See ?

BALTHASAR. Yes, your worship ?

ANTONIO (*exasperated*). Well !

BALTHASAR. Well, your worship, what comes next ?

ANTONIO. Balthasar, you have a thick mind. Can you
not see a joke ?

BALTHASAR. Not easily, your worship. I have great
difficulty in understanding new jokes, but I like to hear
old ones, because then I know when to laugh.

ANTONIO. H'm ! Well, God grant you a wife with an
ancient memory, Balthasar ! If you and she have children,
you should have enough old jokes to last your life. How
many of the company have arrived ?

BALTHASAR. Your worship is the first. My lord Bassanio has not yet returned. Oh, there is a stranger here that fainted by the gate soon after you had gone.

ANTONIO. A stranger! Who is he?

BALTHASAR. I heard his name, but have forgot it. He is an old man, richly dressed, and of great means, but a foreigner. He comes from Venice.

ANTONIO (*immediately agog*). From Venice? I wonder!... Oh, no!... And yet it might be!.., Balthasar, is this stranger the Duke?

BALTHASAR. Duke! What Duke, your worship?

ANTONIO. The Duke of Venice, fool! I dare swear it is he. His grace remembered what took place ten years ago this day, and came to pay me honour. This will denote to you, Balthasar, how old and worthy men should be esteemed. Lead me to his grace that I may give him my loyal salutation.

[BASSANIO *enters hurriedly through the curtains.*

BALTHASAR. Here is my lord!

ANTONIO. Ah, Bassanio, I have news for you, good news!

BASSANIO. Oh! What news? (*To* BALTHASAR.) Has my lady's cousin arrived?

BALTHASAR. He has, my lord, and is now recovering from his journey.

BASSANIO. Let your mistress know that I have returned.

BALTHASAR. I will, my lord. (*Exit.*)

BASSANIO. What is this news, Antonio?

ANTONIO. The Duke is here, come hot with haste to greet me with his love.

BASSANIO (*smiling indulgently*). My dear Antonio, you are mistaken. Portia's cousin is a lawyer, not a duke.

ANTONIO. I am not speaking of Doctor Bellario, but the Duke.

BASSANIO. Duke! What Duke? I beg you, Antonio, not to speak in riddles.

ANTONIO. *Our* Duke! His grace of Venice!

BASSANIO (*astonished*). The Duke of Venice is here!

ANTONIO. He came an hour or two ago and fainted at your very gate. So Balthasar says. His haste had made him weary, I believe.

3

BASSANIO. But what brings the Duke to Belmont?

ANTONIO. To honour me, Bassanio. You may forget your duty to your kinsman, but my sovereign duke remembers it for you.

BASSANIO. Antonio, you are mad!

[BALTHASAR *returns*.

BALTHASAR. My lady bids me tell you, sir, that she is preparing for the masque and begs that you will hasten to make ready for it. (*He turns to go.*)

BASSANIO. Balthasar!

BALTHASAR. My lord!

BASSANIO. What stranger's in the house?

BALTHASAR. Doctor Bellario! . . .

BASSANIO. He is a kinsman of my lady. What stranger came here to-night?

BALTHASAR. I do not remember how he's called, my lord, but will inquire.

BASSANIO. Does he come from Venice?

BALTHASAR. He said so, my lord.

BASSANIO. Is he the Duke?

BALTHASAR. He was not so described nor, indeed, did he look like one.

ANTONIO. How do you know that never saw a duke? Dukes, God forgive me, are but men in looks, and he's a man, this stranger here, and richly dressed, as you yourself did say. " An old man richly dressed and of great means, but a foreigner." Those were your very words.

BASSANIO. Did you say so, Balthasar?

BALTHASAR. I did, my lord. The words are accurately repeated, and they describe him accurately.

BASSANIO. Then go and inquire his name. (*Exit* BALTHASAR.) I beg your pardon, Antonio, if I wounded you with my ungraciousness a moment since.

ANTONIO. It is no matter, Bassanio. Old men must learn to bear their juniors' rudeness with what fortitude they can.

BASSANIO. Were you here when Doctor Bellario came?

ANTONIO. I was. He was scarcely civil to me, but blamed me for his quarrel with Portia. He said the sight of me would fill his mind with bitter memories.

BASSANIO. An ungracious gentleman, then?

ANTONIO. Very.

BASSANIO. Did Portia speak to him of me?

ANTONIO. I did not hear her speak of you. I was listening to what was said of me.

[*A loud knocking is heard on the outer gate.*

BASSANIO. Here come more of our guests, and I am still unready to receive them.

ANTONIO. Wait yet, until Balthasar comes. You are young and can change your dress while older people think about it.

[*A* SERVANT *holds back the curtains, while* NERISSA *and* GRATIANO *enter.*]

BASSANIO. Ah, here are Nerissa and Gratiano in good time.

NERISSA. Portia bade me to be here before her other guests arrived.

BASSANIO. You'll find her in her chamber making ready for a masque.

GRATIANO. Good! I glory in masques!

NERISSA. It is most unseemly at your age to be a masquer or to take so much delight in anything. You should be more sober and think about your grave.

GRATIANO. I am not likely to forget it while you're about.

NERISSA. I wish you would remember to be faithful, then.

GRATIANO. There you go. Fidelity! Always fidelity! But what is fidelity? Lack of imagination! . . .

NERISSA. You'd better not let Portia hear you speaking so. She has little use for flippant talk.

BASSANIO. Come, come, Nerissa. Join Portia in her room.

NERISSA (*mounting the steps*). There'll be an ill end to all this amorous adventuring, master Gratiano. Mark my words for that! If men may philander, then women will philander, too, and the end of that is hard to see.

GRATIANO (*kissing his hand to her*). God's blessing on your cheery talk, my sweet wife! (NERISSA *angrily goes out*.) Her conversation is a continual tale of calamity. I wish her no harm, but if God should see fit to call her hence, I should not resent it.

BASSANIO.   There is an old, rich man from Venice here who is, so Antonio says, the Duke.

GRATIANO.   The Duke of Venice!

[*Re-enter* BALTHASAR.

BASSANIO.   So Antonio says.   Well, Balthasar, what is the stranger's name?

BALTHASAR.   Shylock, my lord!

GRATIANO. } Shylock!
BASSANIO. }

ANTONIO.   Did you say "Shylock"?

BALTHASAR.   That is the stranger's name.   I said it was a foreign one, not easy to remember.

BASSANIO.   Shylock! . . . You're mad, you pompous fool, to say that Shylock's here!

BALTHASAR.   Mad, my lord!   Me, mad!   No, my lord!

BASSANIO.   Who told you this?

BALTHASAR.   My lady's maid.   I bade her ask my mistress for the stranger's name that I might repeat it to you.

BASSANIO.   This is one of Portia's jests.   She has a strange sense of humour.

BALTHASAR.   She did not seem to jest, my lord.   The stranger's come to see his daughter here—Lord Lorenzo's lady!

BASSANIO.   Lorenzo's lady! ,

GRATIANO.   Jessica!

ANTONIO.   The Jew's daughter!

BASSANIO (*to* BALTHASAR).   Where is this man, Shylock?

BALTHASAR.   Resting within, my lord.

BASSANIO.   Bid him come here.

BALTHASAR.   He is not well, my lord.

BASSANIO.   Bid him come here, I tell you.

[BALTHASAR *goes in.*

ANTONIO.   And I believed he was the Duke.

GRATIANO.   Come to do you honour, Antonio!   Perhaps he's come to have another look at your flesh.

BASSANIO.   Why did Portia let him in?

GRATIANO.   Perhaps she did not know it was the Jew. She saw him only once—that day Antonio was tried in Venice.

BASSANIO.   Did Bellario bring him here?

ANTONIO. They did not come together. I saw the Doctor arrive.

[*Enter* LAUNCELOT GOBBO *through the curtains.*

GOBBO. My lord Bassanio!

BASSANIO. What is it now, fool?

GOBBO. My mistress bade me tell you she has changed her mind.

BASSANIO. Go back and tell her I have changed mine, too!

GOBBO. She weeps, my lord.

BASSANIO. Let her weep.

GOBBO. And repents that she used you ill.

BASSANIO. Does she admit that she used me ill?

GOBBO. Yes, my lord, and she bids you come to her again.

BASSANIO. She knows I cannot come to her now. I told her why.

GOBBO (*confidentially*). My lord, she will receive you in her room after the feast is finished. My lady, your wife, has bid her here to dinner. It might be she and you could steal away together. She bade me say so.

BASSANIO. She is a fool to trust you thus, Gobbo, but if ever you betray her to her lord, I'll have the heart out of you.

[SHYLOCK *enters, followed by* BALTHASAR.

GOBBO. I will remember, my lord. (*Sees* SHYLOCK.) Oh, God, the Jew!

SHYLOCK. Gobbo! Launcelot Gobbo! (*Looks round at the company.*) Antonio!

BASSANIO. You are Shylock!

SHYLOCK. And you are Bassanio?

BASSANIO. That is my name.

SHYLOCK (*to* GRATIANO). And you?

GRATIANO. My name is Gratiano.

SHYLOCK. Bassanio's friend. I had forgotten your face. It is a face one might forget. What house is this?

BASSANIO. My house.

SHYLOCK. Your house? I thought it was the house of Portia.

BASSANIO. The lady Portia is my wife.

SHYLOCK. That noble lady is your wife?

BASSANIO. I am her husband and father to her children.

SHYLOCK. I did not know. (*To* GOBBO.) Where is my daughter?

GOBBO. Oh, master Jew, close by! I'll tell her you are here.

SHYLOCK. Go quickly. I am not well! . . . (*He sways and would fall were not* BALTHASAR *by to catch him.*)

GOBBO. I'll go at once. Oh, God, the Jew! (*Exit.*)

ANTONIO. Bid him begone, Bassanio. You cannot have him here.

SHYLOCK. Bear me to my room again, Balthasar. I am not well, and this meeting has not made me better.

BASSANIO. One moment, Jew. I do not wish you to stay here.

SHYLOCK. When morning comes, I'll go.

BASSANIO. I'd have you go to-night.

SHYLOCK. To-night?

BASSANIO. Now.

SHYLOCK. It is late, but I will go if you will give me time to rest myself. My daughter's house is near! . . .

GRATIANO. How, Jew, comes it that you wear these gaudy clothes?

BASSANIO. Yes. Where is your gaberdine, damned Jew?

SHYLOCK (*now recovered from his first distress*). I am not a damned Jew. I am a damned Christian.

BASSANIO. What's this?

GRATIANO. A Christian! You?

SHYLOCK. I am a Christian.

GRATIANO. By conviction?

SHYLOCK. No, sir, by compulsion. I was converted, you'll remember, in the Court at Venice. Antonio here was my godfather.

ANTONIO. I? Godfathered you!

SHYLOCK. You did! You did, my dear Antonio, and rendered me great service in doing it, for all my legal disabilities were removed when you insisted on my christening. I am a citizen of Venice now, and not an alien Jew any more. I'm free to go and come as I please and wear what garments take my fancy. And I am rich again and favoured by the Duke, to whom I have done much service. I thank you, Antonio, for all you did for me,

ANTONIO. God's grace, man, thank not me.

SHYLOCK. I must, Antonio, I must, since all I have I owe to you. Many a time and oft, when I have added richly to my store of wealth or had additions to the honours paid me by the Duke, I've thought of you and thanked you heartily, Antonio.

GRATIANO. Does the Duke honour you?

ANTONIO. That never honoured me?

SHYLOCK. I am now a member of the Senate.

ANTONIO. You, a Senator!

SHYLOCK. I thank you for it, good Antonio. It's strange that I should meet you here so soon, for when I told the Duke seven days ago that I was venturing forth from Venice and wondered if I'd meet you here in Belmont, he did not well remember you—he's growing old, so you must pardon him—but I recalled you to his memory, whereon he spoke of you.

ANTONIO. What did he say?

SHYLOCK. He said—I have his very words—" I remember now. A tiresome gentleman who preached!"

ANTONIO. Preached!

SHYLOCK. No, I'm wrong. The word was " moralized." Moralized! That was the word. " A tiresome gentleman who moralized!"

ANTONIO. 'Tis false. I'm not a moralizer.

BASSANIO. Enough of this! Honoured or not honoured, you're still a Jew to me, Shylock. If you were God Himself, I'd call you Jew, and bid you leave my house.

SHYLOCK. I am not God Himself, that's sure, but if I were, you would do well to call me Jew! . . .

GRATIANO. This is blasphemy!

BASSANIO. I'll have no quibbling here. Go!

SHYLOCK. I'll go, my lord. My presence cannot give you less pleasure than yours gives me.

BASSANIO. Be careful with your tongue, Jew.

SHYLOCK. Were I less careful with my tongue, Bassanio, than you were with your friends, I'd long ago have hanged.

BASSANIO. What's your meaning now?

SHYLOCK. Ask your kinsman here, Antonio, who lent

you money ne'er repaid, and was forgot the moment it was lent. Is that not so, Antonio?

ANTONIO. That's no affair of yours, Jew.

SHYLOCK. No? Three thousand ducats that were mine were lent to him on your security. I never had it back. Your life was mine. I did not get that either. But Bassanio had as little thought for your life as he had for my ducats. There is a sin, Bassanio, that stretches far beyond most sins, ingratitude, and you are deeply practised in it.

BASSANIO. Be silent, cur!

SHYLOCK. I am a citizen of Venice and entitled to civility from you, my lord.

BASSANIO. There's no civility for you nor any Jew. Your race is outlawed from the world's compassion. There is not, nor ever will be, peace 'twixt us and you. You are a Jew.

SHYLOCK. I am a Jew! . . .

GRATIANO. Turned Christian!

SHYLOCK. Turned Christian by compulsion. I had no choice in this, whether to be a Jew or a Christian, even as you, Gratiano, had no choice in your birth. You are a Christian for the reason I'm a Jew, that you were born so. Had you been born, as I was born, a Jew! . . .

GRATIANO. That could never have been. A Turk, perhaps, and there is much that is commendable in Turks, but a Jew, no! Never! I should have foresworn birth rather than be born a Jew.

SHYLOCK. We are not masters of our birth, Gratiano. God does not stop to ask us what our nationality shall be.

GRATIANO. God is wise and makes the best of His material. That which He loves, He makes into Christians. That which He dislikes, He makes into Jews.

BASSANIO. Let's have no more argument. Come, Jew, make ready to go!

SHYLOCK. I have not done, my lord. I meant to say that though I am a Jew, I would not in my most extremity have left my friend as you left Antonio. You are a pretty gentleman, my lord Bassanio, to deck yourself with bought nobility that came to Belmont here to hunt a fortune with borrowed means, and left your friend to pay your debt, if need be, with his life.

BASSANIO. By God I'll bear no more of this.

SHYLOCK. I am a Jew, you say, and you a Christian. I wish your Saviour joy of you!

BASSANIO. Out, I tell you, lest I throw you to my dogs.

                  [PORTIA, *in her richest dress, enters.*

PORTIA. My lord! What noise is this?

BASSANIO. This man—do you know him?

PORTIA. I do. He is Shylock.

ANTONIO. That tried to take my life.

PORTIA. Yes, but failed, Antonio. Come, Shylock, you should not be here in this cold air. Balthasar, bear him back to his chamber.

BASSANIO. Madam, I have commanded him to leave this house to-night.

PORTIA. And why, my lord?

BASSANIO. Because it is my will.

PORTIA. But I, my lord, will otherwise. Come, Shylock!

ANTONIO. How can you keep him here when I am by?

PORTIA. Are you a reason why I should be uncivil to an old man, sick at my gate? . . .

BASSANIO. But this is Shylock, the Jew!

PORTIA. Well? We had our quarrel with him, which we won. Are we to keep it up forever?

ANTONIO. I can keep it up, and will!

PORTIA. I am ashamed of you, Antonio, to be so rancorous, and you so near the grave. I tremble for you on the Judgment Day.

BASSANIO. I tell you yet again, Portia, I will not tolerate this Jew! . . .

SHYLOCK. I pray you, madam, give me leave to go from hence.

PORTIA. No. You are not well. The hour is late. You'll stay until the morning.

BASSANIO. Madam!

PORTIA. My lord!

BASSANIO. Be warned! Think well of what you say and what you do!

PORTIA. I have thought well, Bassanio!

BASSANIO. If he remains within this house to-night, I will not stay with you.

SHYLOCK. Madam! . . .

PORTIA. Your presence, my lord, has not been so comforting that I am likely to mourn your absence. My cousin, Doctor Bellario, will speak to you about the money you have wasted.

[*Enter* JESSICA *from the outer court. She is very beautiful, but is still the mean little sweep she was when she ran away with* LORENZO. *Her beauty is slightly marred by lines of discontent about her eyes and mouth, and she is more obviously sensual than she was ten years ago. She goes to* BASSANIO.]

JESSICA. What tale is this I hear from Gobbo? . . . Oh, God, my father!

SHYLOCK (*profoundly moved by the sight of her*). Jessica! My little Jessica!

JESSICA. Why did you come here?

SHYLOCK. I came in search of you, but sickened at this lady's gate.

PORTIA. I have received your father as my guest, Jessica, and wish that he will stay with us 'til he is well again.

JESSICA. But that's impossible, Portia. Father, you must go back to Venice.

SHYLOCK. Why? Will you not receive me?

JESSICA. I cannot, father. Lorenzo does not love you.

SHYLOCK. Do you love me?

JESSICA. You are my father.

SHYLOCK. Do *you* love me?

JESSICA. Your house was hard! . . .

SHYLOCK. I loved you, Jessica, as no man ever loved his child, and I dreamt great dreams for you, but you destroyed them.

JESSICA. You were too hard, father. I could not love you.

SHYLOCK. Ungrateful girl, well were you wed to a Christian gentleman. You fled from me that loved you, and stole my money to endow a man that daily made a mock of me and my religion. And since that day I've heard no word from you, nor have you ever questioned was I alive or dead.

JESSICA. I did not love you, father. I cannot love by rule, but as I'm swayed.

SHYLOCK. So. Did you love your mother, Jessica?

JESSICA. I do not well remember her.

SHYLOCK. When Tubal, my friend, came to me in Venice after you had fled and told me of your wasteful wanderings, there was one thing you did that tore my heart in pieces.

JESSICA. I do not now remember what I did. 'Tis very long ago.

SHYLOCK. I have not forgotten, nor will I ever forget. I'll tell you, girl, what it was that killed me here. (*Touching his breast.*)

BASSANIO. Well, tell her somewhere else.

PORTIA. My lord, you're strangely lacking in civility.

SHYLOCK (*to* PORTIA). I will not trespass on your hospitality too long, my lady. (*To* JESSICA.) Your mother, while I was still a bachelor, gave me a ring, a turquoise ring, the first of all the gifts I had from her, and I valued it, and loved it more than all I had. You stole it from me, Jessica, the night you fled from Venice with your lover, lord Lorenzo.

JESSICA. I'll look for it and give it back to you again.

SHYLOCK. You will not find it nor can you ever give it back to me. So little value had your mother's ring for you, Jessica, though it was very dear to me, that you sold it for a monkey there in Genoa. O, God of Israel, how that hurt my heart!

JESSICA. I did not think. I pray you, father, return to Venice now.

SHYLOCK. I've heard that you have children. How many?

JESSICA. Three, father. Three sons:

SHYLOCK. Three sons! You have been blessed, Jessica. How are they named?

JESSICA. The first is called Lorenzo, for his father! . . .

SHYLOCK. His father! Yes?

JESSICA. The second! . . .

SHYLOCK. The second, yes! Yes, the second?

JESSICA. Is called for his godfather here, Antonio.

SHYLOCK. Antonio! I see! Godfathering's a general

habit with you, Antonio. First the grandsire and then the grandson. Well? How is the third named?

JESSICA. After my lord Bassanio.

SHYLOCK. Your lord Bassanio! Did you forget my name?

JESSICA. My husband does not like Jews.

SHYLOCK. Yet he loves you?

JESSICA. I am a woman.

SHYLOCK. Have your children ever heard of me, their grandsire?

JESSICA. We do not speak of you, father.

SHYLOCK. Do they like Jews?

GRATIANO. I'll answer you for that, old Shylock. I heard the littlest one, that's called after you, Bassanio, cry as he strided up and down the passage to Lorenzo's house, "Down with the Jews! Down with the dirty Jews!"

SHYLOCK (*after a moment's silence*). Yet they are Jews.

GRATIANO. How now, Jews?

ANTONIO. I saw them christened at the font for little Christians, and the one that's named after me has a nose the Pope himself might wear.

SHYLOCK. Yet are they Jews, for they have my blood in their little Christian hearts.

GRATIANO. But you said that you were a Christian, too.

SHYLOCK. Do you then acknowledge me to be a Christian?

GRATIANO. I do not know. I am weak on theology. What do you say, Antonio? You godfathered him.

ANTONIO. He is, perhaps, a Christian in law, but not as one born to it. A half-and-half sort of a Christian, with one leg in heaven and t'other in hell!

BASSANIO. I care not where his legs may be so that they be not here. Come, Jew-Christian, Christian-Jew, are you going?

PORTIA. I have already answered that for you, my lord. This gentleman will stay with us to-night.

BASSANIO. Then *I* shall go to-night.

PORTIA. That's as you please, Bassanio!

[*Enter* DOCTOR BELLARIO *from the house.*

PORTIA. Here's my cousin, come in time to greet you before you go. This, Bassanio, is Doctor Bellario.

BELLARIO.   It seems I missed you on the road.

BASSANIO.   Missed me ?

BELLARIO.   You went to meet me, so your servant said.

BASSANIO.   True ! I somehow lost my way in the dark.

BELLARIO.   You have not yet learned your way about Belmont ?

BASSANIO.   I know it very well.

BELLARIO.   Ha !

BASSANIO.   I'm glad to meet you, sir, and welcome you to Belmont.   But first, let me rid the house of this pernicious Jew ! . . .

BELLARIO.   Who ? Shylock ?

BASSANIO.   You know him, then ?

PORTIA.   They met an hour or two ago, Bassanio, while you were losing your way.

BELLARIO (*to* SHYLOCK).   You were the plaintiff in that suit against Antonio.

SHYLOCK.   I was.

BELLARIO.   A most interesting case—most interesting, but shockingly handled from your point of view.   My dear sir, a man who is his own counsel has a fool for a client.   If you had engaged me to plead your case, I think Antonio here would be considerably lighter than he is.

ANTONIO.   God's grace, sir !

BELLARIO (*taking hold of* ANTONIO).   A pound of flesh ! After all, it isn't much.

ANTONIO.   By your leave sir, it's enough !

GRATIANO.   Truly, Antonio, for there is scarcely enough meat on your bones to make up to the full of a pound. You are a very lean man.

BELLARIO.   Not so lean as he would be if Shylock had had his way.   Eh, Antonio ? Ha, ha, ha ! (*Slaps* ANTONIO *on the back without, however, provoking any mirth from* ANTONIO.) I wish you'd engaged me, Shylock. I'd have won your case for you.

ANTONIO.   By our Lady, this lawyer talks of pounds of a man's flesh as if they were pounds of potatoes.

BELLARIO.   I heard you say, Bassanio, you wished to rid the house of a Jew ?

BASSANIO.   Yes.   This Jew, Shylock !

BELLARIO.   But he's a Christian now—legally.   You'd

best be careful how you call a Christian a Jew, especially
if he is a Jew. He could sue you in the Courts for de-
famation of character. Shylock, if you bring a suit against
him, I hope you'll retain me.

BASSANIO. I like not this sort of banter, sir.

BELLARIO. I guessed as much from gazing on you, my
good Bassanio. How comes it that you missed me on
the road when there is only one road leads that way?

BASSANIO. I do not know. 'Twas dark.

BELLARIO. But light enough for me to find my way.
Your eyes, perhaps, mislead you, Bassanio. You should
have them attended to by a surgeon.

[*Enter* BALTHASAR.

BALTHASAR. Madam, the guests assemble.

PORTIA. Bid them enter. Come, Shylock, return to
your chamber. You will not wish to see our festival
while you are sick and tired.

SHYLOCK. Madam, I have a daughter here. It is to
her house I should go.

JESSICA. My husband would not welcome you.

PORTIA. Your husband is not at home, Jessica.

JESSICA. No, Portia, but when he returns! . . .

PORTIA. I understand! There's no place else for you,
Shylock, to-night. You must stay here.

SHYLOCK. I am your servant, madam.

PORTIA. Good-night, Shylock.

SHYLOCK. Good-night, Portia. (*He raises her hand to
his lips and then goes out.*)

PORTIA (*to* BALTHASAR). Let the guests come in.

BASSANIO. By God, my lady, I'll bear no more of
this! . . .

[BALTHASAR *has drawn the curtains, and the guests in
rich and gay clothes can be seen crossing the outer
courtyard.*]

PORTIA. Our guests assemble, my lord!

BASSANIO. I care not for our guests or you! . . .

[PORTIA *goes forward to meet the guests, who enter in
quick succession. There is much animation, and
presently the sound of music is heard. The scene
gradually fills up.*]

BELLARIO (*aside to* BASSANIO). You'd best be friends

with Shylock, young gentleman. Your fortunes are askew, and he may be willing to lend you money.

BASSANIO. Lend me money! . . .

BELLARIO. S-s-s-sh! . . . (*He goes to* PORTIA *and mingles with the guests.*)

JESSICA. Bassanio! (*No answer.*) Bassanio!

BASSANIO. What! Are you still here?

JESSICA. Why, yes, Bassanio. I am a guest to-night.

BASSANIO. Then go and be one.

JESSICA (*reproachfully*). Bassanio! Bassanio!

BASSANIO. What, hussy?

JESSICA. I sent a message to you to-night by Gobbo.

BASSANIO. I got it, I got it!

JESSICA. But gave no answer to it.

BASSANIO. There was no answer.

JESSICA. Oh, Bassanio! . . .

BASSANIO. Be quiet, fool! Someone will hear you!

JESSICA. Come to me to-night. I'll promise you all you desire.

BASSANIO. You were not so complaisant when I saw you last.

JESSICA. I only meant to tease you.

BASSANIO. Tease me, by God! I'm not a man that can endure teasing. If you wish to have my love, Jessica, be circumspect and yielding. I have no time for teasing ways.

JESSICA. I'll do whatever you bid me, Bassanio.

BASSANIO. This way of wooing women with subtlety and coy advances and delicate retreats—I'm not for that, but for plain, blunt love, and be done with it. I had my enough of teasing ways when I was young, but now I'm for decision, sudden and abrupt. Will you love? Then love! Will you not love? Then go and be damned! Do you understand me, Jessica? No dalliance, no whimsy-whamsies, no long entreaties, but swift surrender and unresisting love for me.

JESSICA. Yes, Bassanio, I understand and will obey you in everything.

BASSANIO. I like obedient women. I'll come to you to-night. Soon after twelve, we'll steal away together. Do you hear?

JESSICA. Yes, Bassanio.

[*There is a movement in the crowd, and* PORTIA *leading* DOCTOR BELLARIO, *comes forward.*]

PORTIA. Dear friends, let us go in. Bassanio, will you bring Jessica?

[*She goes out with* DOCTOR BELLARIO, *followed by* BASSANIO *and* JESSICA, *and the rest of the guests. The stage is left empty for a few moments. We still hear the music, and can see the coloured lights in the courtyard.* LAUNCELOT GOBBO *sneaks into the outer yard and then into the inner one. He looks about him, and then goes towards the steps leading into the house. As he does so,* SHYLOCK *appears at the head of them.* GOBBO *gives a gulp of alarm.*]

SHYLOCK. Gobbo!

GOBBO. Sir!

SHYLOCK (*descending the steps*). You serve my daughter and her husband, do you not?

GOBBO. Yes, sir, I do, sir. Truly I do.

SHYLOCK. Is their house far from here?

GOBBO. A goodly step, sir.

SHYLOCK. Will you take me to it?

GOBBO. But my lady, your daughter, she is here, at the festival!

SHYLOCK. I know. Gobbo, I would like to see my grandsons. Will you not gratify my wish?

GOBBO. But, sir, if my mistress will not! . . .

SHYLOCK. I will pay you well, Gobbo, and no one need know. They'll be asleep now, will they not?

GOBBO. I hope so, sir.

SHYLOCK. Then gratify me this much, and I'll reward you well.

GOBBO. But I cannot come on the instant, sir. My lady bade me wait for her here. She has instructions for me.

SHYLOCK. How long are you to wait?

GOBBO. Until she sends for me. Women are sometimes dilatory, sir.

SHYLOCK. This festival will last the night?

GOBBO. It will, sir, though some will not last with it.

SHYLOCK. When you have had my daughter's message, send for me and take me to her house! . . .

GOBBO. I dare not, sir.

SHYLOCK. I'll pay you well, Gobbo, and none shall know I've seen my grandsons but yourself and me. I'll look at them and come away again. You'll gratify me? (GOBBO *hesitates.* SHYLOCK *produces a purse and clinks the money in it.*) Well, Gobbo?

GOBBO. I will, sir. After all, it is a Christian act to let a grandsire see his grandsons.

SHYLOCK. Even though he be a Jew. Go, Gobbo, and get your message, and come again for me.

[GOBBO *goes in, and* SHYLOCK *is left in the dusk, listening to the music.*]

THE THIRD ACT

[*The scene is a pillared hall in* PORTIA'S *house. When the curtain ascends, the guests are found dancing to lively music.* PORTIA *and* DOCTOR BELLARIO *are dancing together.* BASSANIO *is dancing with* JESSICA. GRATIANO *is dancing with a young and pretty girl.* NERISSA *is sitting with* ANTONIO, *to whom, however, she pays very little attention, for she is jealously watching her husband and his partner.*]

ANTONIO. I am uncomfortable, Nerissa, when I remember that that Jew is here, a room or two away from me. I do not like the thought, and I take it very ill from Portia that she keeps him here.

NERISSA. Do you see that girl with Gratiano?

ANTONIO. What girl? Where?

NERISSA. Dancing now with Gratiano. Who is she?

ANTONIO. I do not know, Nerissa, and I was talking of the Jew.

NERISSA. I think her face surpasses all I've ever seen in ugliness.

ANTONIO. Whose face?

NERISSA. Hers—that hussy with the tawny hair who ogles Gratiano with her squinting eyes.

ANTONIO (*peering at the girl*). Does she squint?

NERISSA. Most vilely. And he squints who cannot see that she squints. She is a smirking wench that has no modesty of mind or shape. She'll die in bad repute, if I know anything, and live in it, too.

ANTONIO. Has she done you an injury?

NERISSA. Any woman who interests my husband does me an injury.

ANTONIO. I fear he does not make you happy, Nerissa.

NERISSA. He does not.

ANTONIO. Then why continue in his house?

NERISSA. Because I love him, fool. Do you remember how my lady won Bassanio?

ANTONIO. I do, and have good cause to remember it, for that was how the Jew! . . .

NERISSA. Oh, hold your peace about the Jew!

ANTONIO. Faith, he nearly held a piece of me.

NERISSA. At last, Antonio, you have made a joke. There's hope for you, but Jew me no Jew, I beg. My mistress' father left a will! . . .

ANTONIO. I remember.

NERISSA. A foolish old man's will that you might leave—whereby her hand was given to him who chose the right one of three caskets.

ANTONIO. Yes. One of gold, one of silver, and one of lead. Who chose the last, won Portia.

NERISSA. So. Her father, being old and mad, God help him, thought by this device to save her from fortune-hunters.

ANTONIO. It was not a successful device.

NERISSA. It was not, for never on this earth was there a fortune-hunter equal to Bassanio. But my lady loved him for his handsome looks and bearing, and I loved Gratiano for the same. How do you think Bassanio chose the right casket?

ANTONIO. I've heard the story. There's a ballad made of it. By wisdom, I suppose, or good fortune.

NERISSA. By rubbish. He has not enough wit in his head to make a sensible choice of anything. I told him which to choose.

ANTONIO. You told him! . . .

NERISSA. Portia hinted that I should, and I was nothing loth, for if she had not got him, I should not have had Gratiano.

ANTONIO. What loss would that have been?

NERISSA. Old man, anything you want but do not get, is a loss, whether it be good or bad. I told Bassanio which casket he must choose, and thus he won Portia.

ANTONIO. And so her father's will was defeated. The

young always circumvent us, scheme how we may. But there were other suitors, were there not ?

NERISSA. Nine in all, my lord Bassanio in the number.

ANTONIO. How was it none of them chose the right casket ?

NERISSA. Some declined to make choice and went away. The rest—I told them which to choose ! . . .

ANTONIO. But they chose wrongly.

NERISSA. I know. I told them which to choose.

ANTONIO. Then you made this marriage up betwixt Portia and Bassanio.

NERISSA. At her desire, I did, and I am well rewarded for my work. My husband dances with a smirking maid— if she be a maid—while I sit here, neglected, with no one to talk to but you.

ANTONIO (*indignantly getting up*). Well, Nerissa, if sitting here's no fun for you, it's not much fun for me.

[*The music ends, and the guests scatter.* PORTIA *and* BELLARIO *come forward, and so do* BASSANIO *and* JESSICA.]

BASSANIO (*to* PORTIA). Are you determined that the Jew shall stay ?

PORTIA. I am.

BASSANIO. This is a planned affront to me, Portia.

PORTIA. If you persist in thinking so, it must be so.

BASSANIO. I beg you to send him away.

PORTIA. Do not ask me again, Bassanio. I have resolved that he shall stay.

BASSANIO. Why ?

PORTIA. It is my whim.

BASSANIO. Whim !

PORTIA. You may call it so. I do not choose to turn an old, sick man away because we had a quarrel with him long ago. But call it a whim, if that will please you.

BASSANIO. I will not ask you again !

PORTIA. I beg that you won't. (*She turns to* BELLARIO.) Well, cousin, have you enjoyed the dance ?

BELLARIO. Heartily, my dear.

BASSANIO (*aside to* JESSICA). An hour from now, we'll steal from this. If she must have her whim, then I'll have mine.

JESSICA. Of whom are you speaking, Bassanio?

BASSANIO. No matter. I'll stay with you to-night.

PORTIA. Jessica!

JESSICA. Yes, Portia.

PORTIA. Come here and sit with me.

JESSICA. I shall disturb your conversation with your cousin.

PORTIA. He will not mind such sweet disturbance. Come here and sit by me. (JESSICA *does so.*)

BELLARIO. I have something to say to Bassanio which I could not say before, and now's a good time to say it. I'll join you here again when the dance begins.

      [He goes off to speak to BASSANIO.

PORTIA. Do you regret Lorenzo's absence, Jessica?

JESSICA. Oh, yes, I do.

PORTIA. And never wish to have him stay away?

JESSICA. Why, no. He is my husband.

PORTIA. That's why I asked you. You still are pretty, Jessica.

JESSICA. It's kind of you to say so, my lady.

PORTIA. And you have soft and gentle ways. What were your thoughts when first you saw your father here to-night?

JESSICA. I knew not what to think.

PORTIA. He's rich again.

JESSICA. So I've been told. Was it not settled by the law that all he has shall come to Lorenzo and me when he dies?

PORTIA. That was a condition of the judgment given against him. Antonio made it.

JESSICA. I'm glad that he is rich again.

PORTIA. Have you no love for him, Jessica?

JESSICA. My father? (*Shrugs her shoulders.*)

PORTIA. You must love Lorenzo very much.

JESSICA. Yes. Yes, I do love Lorenzo.

PORTIA. What do you think of my husband?

JESSICA. Lord Bassanio!

PORTIA. That is his name.

JESSICA. I have not thought of him more than I ought to think. He's a handsome man.

PORTIA. He was a handsome man, and had a trick of

lovely words, with which he wooed and won me. But now he repeats himself.

JESSICA. He speaks in a very gallant and fascinating way to women.

PORTIA. Is that how he speaks to you?

JESSICA. Oh, no! His manner's always courteous to me, but I've been told his syllables are full of charm when he is bent on wooing.

PORTIA. From whom did you hear this?

JESSICA. From Lorenzo and Nerissa and her husband, Gratiano. From you, and all who know him.

PORTIA. He has not told you so himself?

JESSICA. Oh, no! He has respect for you and Lorenzo.

PORTIA. That's new to me. Shall I send your father to you in the morning?

JESSICA. I beg you, no. Bid him go back to Venice.

PORTIA. He's such an old man, Jessica, and gentler now than when he sued Antonio. He has not seen your children, and he would like to see them.

JESSICA. I dare not have him while Lorenzo's gone.

PORTIA. Bassanio's angry with me because I keep your father here, and threatens he will quarrel with me if I let him stay. Will you not take your father home with you to-night that I may keep peace with my husband?

JESSICA. To-night?

PORTIA. Now. I'll send for him. There's nowhere else for him to go.

JESSICA. Oh no, I cannot consent to that. Let him remain with you to-night. I'll think what's best to do to-morrow. Not to-night.

PORTIA. Why, what's to do, Jessica? You shake with apprehension.

JESSICA. I cannot have my father home to-night.

PORTIA. Well, then, we'll leave him here until the morning. Look! The dance begins again. Come, Gratiano, dance with me. Who'll dance with Jessica?

BASSANIO. I will, with all my heart.

BELLARIO. Bassanio, let this dance go by. I've something more to say to you.

BASSANIO. But Jessica! . . .

JESSICA. This gentleman will dance with me.

[*She goes off with a guest. The music begins again and continues, with dancing, through the next scene.*]

BASSANIO. Your looks are grave, Bellario.

BELLARIO. Yours should be graver! My cousin's fortune is almost dissipated.

BASSANIO. A man must live and have enjoyment.

BELLARIO. The world would be more comfortable, Bassanio, if we could make our life and our pleasure equal in duration with our means. To die when the last coin is spent and the last pleasure tasted would no doubt be an excellent end. But Heaven is not always so exact as that, my cousin, and you are likely to outlast your means by a long time. There's little left.

BASSANIO. Can we not raise more money?

BELLARIO. On what?

BASSANIO. On anything.

BELLARIO. I fear that your reputation as a debtor, Bassanio, does you little credit. There's only one way to keep means and life on some sort of equality.

BASSANIO. And what's that?

BELLARIO. Thrift—inexorable thrift.

BASSANIO. I like it not.

BELLARIO. I was afraid you wouldn't, but, like or not like, you must intrigue with thrift, Bassanio, if you are not to lose your wife's estate. You have a pretty gift for spending what's not your own.

BASSANIO. I do not catch your meaning.

BELLARIO. I remember that you won my cousin's hand with money that was borrowed, but was not repaid.

BASSANIO. I've heard more than enough about that money. Antonio has me deafened with his reminders of it, and now this Jew comes to keep the world in memory of it. God, but I'd give ten times the sum to have him out of this.

BELLARIO. You mean that you would get someone else to give ten times the sum.

BASSANIO. Have it as you will.

BELLARIO. Why are you so anxious to expel him from your house? A Jew's a harmless, necessary person. Since we cannot be thrifty for ourselves, we must have Jews to be thrifty for us. ˜I am a lawyer, Bassanio, and therefore superior to common prejudice, and I am able to look upon Jews dispassionately and even with some affection. A Jew will trust you if you will trust him. He is a useful member of society if he is kept in some subjection, but not in too close subjection. My own view of government, Bassanio, is one which grants a moderate amount of freedom to everybody—not too much, and not too little. Mediocrity in everything is my motto. That's why I am a lawyer. Come, Bassanio, make friends with Shylock, and borrow some money from him.

BASSANIO. I have a loathing for this man that makes me lose my judgment. It is not anything about which I can argue. I loathe him. That's all, but it's enough.

BELLARIO. Has he done wrong to you?

BASSANIO. No, I've done wrong to him. If I were on the dizziest edge of poverty, and he should save me from it, I'd loathe him still.

BELLARIO. But would you let him save you?

BASSANIO. Perhaps.

BELLARIO. As a lawyer, I dislike these passions, although, of course, they provide me with a livelihood. I hoped you'd make a friend of Shylock! . . .

BASSANIO. He will not lend money to me.

BELLARIO. I'll sound him on it. A Jew will always lend money to a Christian, even if he despises him, when there's some social advantage to be got from it.

BASSANIO. No, I'll have none of that. I will not have him prowling here as the price of his loan. Usury, yes, but friendship, no. Doctor Bellario, persuade my wife to send him hence. You have influence with her. I have none.

BELLARIO. That, I think, 's not possible. Some woman's chivalry makes her over-scrupulous. There's less imagination in women than there is in men.

BASSANIO. I've told her I'll not stay if he remains.

BELLARIO. Tush, man, to-morrow he'll be gone.

BASSANIO. But her authority'll remain. If she can disregard my wish in this to-day, she'll disregard it in some other cause to-morrow and to-morrow and to-morrow.

BELLARIO. A loan, at reasonable interest, would put your house in order. I'll talk to Shylock in the morning.

BASSANIO. If he is here to-morrow, I'll take no loan from him nor live with Portia any more.

BELLARIO. Here's obstinacy for you!

BASSANIO. Will you yourself not lend what money's needed?

BELLARIO. No. I do not like the security.

BASSANIO. God, man, how you insult me with every word you speak.

BELLARIO. I do not like you, Bassanio, nor have I heard any accounts of you that show you in a state to make me like you.

BASSANIO. Then damn your help and good advice! . . .

BELLARIO. As you please! (*Turns to go.*)

BASSANIO. Stay! I'm hasty in my speech, and you provoked me.

BELLARIO. Make no mistake, cousin Bassanio, about me. I do not like you. You are one of those men that trade upon their looks and make poor fools of women fond of them. There's nothing to you, my friend, but a handsome face that will soon be disfigured by excess. When that's done, you will sue for women's favours and be refused. That's the rake's purgatory. I pity you that in your old age you'll have no memory of decent deeds to comfort your decline! . . .

BASSANIO. That's my affair, not yours. If you mistrust and hate me so, why do you offer to help me against the Jew?

BELLARIO. Because I have affection for my cousin, Portia, and that affection's stirred by her distress with you. She seems still to care for you. I think it's a pity, but she does. I have suggested that perhaps she could obtain remission of her marriage from the Pope! . . .

BASSANIO. Sir, you presume upon your years.

BELLARIO. That's true. One does. I'll speak to Portia about the loan from Shylock. She may be willing to approach him.

[*The music ends, as he speaks, and some of the dancers enter. JESSICA comes to BASSANIO as he is about to go out. DOCTOR BELLARIO has already gone.*]

JESSICA. Does Portia suspect that I love you?

BASSANIO. I do not know.

JESSICA. She spoke oddly to me now, but I swore that I only loved Lorenzo.

BASSANIO. And do you love Lorenzo?

JESSICA. You know that I love you, not him. I cannot bear his moonstruck talk of music. Night after night he reads his verses to me, until I want to scream, but dare not, lest he say I have no soul. Oh, I like rude, rough men, that catch a woman without pity and use her how they will. I hate this soft musician's love that will not hurt me except with phrases.

[*Enter* GRATIANO *and* NERISSA.

GRATIANO. Bassanio!

BASSANIO. Yes, Gratiano.

GRATIANO. I have a scheme! . . .

NERISSA. 'Twas I that thought of it.

GRATIANO. True, she thought of it, but I approved it. It's this. But wait, Jessica is here.

BASSANIO. What odds for that?

GRATIANO. It concerns her father.

BASSANIO. No matter. Go on.

JESSICA. I'll come again when you are done.   (*Exit*.)

GRATIANO. It is a scheme to rid you of Shylock and reconcile you to your wife without the loss of dignity to either.

BASSANIO. That will be difficult.

GRATIANO. Not so difficult as you imagine. Shylock does not know who Portia is.

BASSANIO. He knows she is my wife.

GRATIANO. But nothing more. He does not know she is the lawyer that defrauded him of old Antonio's flesh. He saw her once in Venice, in the Duke's Court, and thought she was a man, as indeed, we did ourselves, Bassanio, and has not seen her since until to-day.

NERISSA. Nor does he know I was her clerk. He thought that I, too, was a man.

GRATIANO. I wish you were.

NERISSA. If I were a man, as you're a man, I'd break your skull!

BASSANIO. I pray you, keep this connubial conversation for another time. I have enough of it at home, without importing any.

GRATIANO. The scheme is this. We'll tell Shylock who Portia is, and he'll be so enraged, he'll go at once without a word.

BASSANIO. That scheme's no good. He'll not believe it.

GRATIANO. He will not doubt our word!

NERISSA. He will. I would myself. Some other scheme! . . . (*She goes apart to cogitate.*)

BASSANIO. Time was when women gave obedience to their husbands.

GRATIANO. When was that time?

BASSANIO. I do not know.

GRATIANO. Nor I nor anyone.

BASSANIO. In Eastern lands, they say, women give strict obedience to their lords.

GRATIANO. The East is far away, Bassanio, or I would go to it.

BASSANIO. I'd like to have an Eastern wife—a little, clinging, dark-haired, soft, obedient wife, that came when called and went when told. These tall, blond women claim too much equality with us. I know a little, clinging, dark-haired woman! . . .

GRATIANO. Has she a sister like herself?

BASSANIO. She is content to love when she is bid— a little, servile, unassertive thing! . . .

GRATIANO. What is her name?

BASSANIO. Her name! No matter! . . .

GRATIANO. Is her name Jessica?

BASSANIO. No matter!

GRATIANO. I wish the Jew had gotten twins when he got her.

NERISSA. I have another scheme, a most valiant and noble scheme! . . .

GRATIANO. Say it out, then!

NERISSA. We'll try Antonio a second time.

BASSANIO. Try Antonio! . . .

NERISSA. As he was tried in Venice. We'll persuade Portia that Doctor Bellario would like to see her in her lawyer's robes and hear how she conducted old Antonio's trial.

BASSANIO. Well, what then?

NERISSA. Meanwhile, we'll have the Jew in hiding

here on some pretext, and when he sees her enter in her robes, he'll recognize her and depart.

BASSANIO. But he may not depart.

NERISSA. He will, for he is full of pride. Besides, we'll make such game of him in trial that he will not wish to stay and see it ended. Doctor Bellario can be the Duke, Antonio, himself! . . .

BASSANIO. Who'll play the Jew?

GRATIANO. Let me. I warrant you I'll make a fierce and bloody-minded Jew and shrug my shoulders and spread my hands—O, I'll be a Jew to deceive Moses.

NERISSA. Here comes Portia. Go, Gratiano, and instruct Antonio in his part, and when we have persuaded Portia to play, I'll go with her to help her with her robes. While we are gone, get the Jew here and hide him in a corner.

GRATIANO. For this, my heart's delight, I'll love you as I should.

[*Exit* GRATIANO. *As he goes out,* PORTIA *enters.*

PORTIA. Where's Gratiano going?

NERISSA. To find Antonio. We have a plan to entertain your cousin, Portia.

PORTIA. I've come to find him. Our guests are in the garden, watching a masque. Will you not come and see it, Nerissa?

NERISSA. Presently I will, but now! . . .

PORTIA. Bassanio, we should be with our guests.

NERISSA. Bassanio has confessed to me, Portia, his grief that you and he have quarrelled. He wishes to be friends with you again.

PORTIA. Do you, Bassanio?

NERISSA. See how his tongue misgives him. He cannot speak, because he feels so much. Come, Portia, come, Bassanio, be friends.

PORTIA. With all my heart, Bassanio, I will be friends with you, if you'll be friends with me.

[NERISSA *puts their hands together, and* PORTIA *kisses* BASSANIO.]

PORTIA. Have either of you seen my cousin?

NERISSA. Is he not with your other guests?

PORTIA. No. I came to take him to the masque.

NERISSA. He'll come presently. Meantime, we'll tell you of our plan to entertain him. Bassanio heard him say he'd like to see you in your lawyer's robes.

PORTIA. My lawyer's robes!

NERISSA. Those that you wore in Venice when Antonio was tried. And I bethought me of a little comedy we'd play to please him.

PORTIA. Yes?

NERISSA. We'll try Antonio a second time, and you. shall show your cousin how you won his case.

PORTIA. But Shylock's here! . . .

BASSANIO. Why must we always think of Shylock? . . .

NERISSA. He is not here—in this room. He's in another room, and will not see our play or even know of it.

PORTIA. Do you think my cousin will be pleased with this?

NERISSA. He told Bassanio so.

PORTIA. Then you have spoke to him about it.

NERISSA. We have. Is it not so, my lord.

BASSANIO. It is.

NERISSA. You have your robes still?

PORTIA. I keep them in my chamber, and sometimes, when I am alone, I put them on and am a man again. And your robes, too, Nerissa, I have them safe. You'll be my clerk!

NERISSA. No, no, clerking's a poor, unprofitable trade. I got Gratiano for my pay! . . .

PORTIA. Hush, hush, Nerissa! To-night's a festival. Forget you have a husband.

BASSANIO. Can you remember what you said before the Duke?

PORTIA. As much as I shall need. Come, Nerissa, let's get ready for the play. We'll show my cousin how we once were men.

[*Exeunt.*

BASSANIO. Now for the Jew! Where's Gratiano? (*He sees* BALTHASAR.) Balthasar! Balthasar!

BALTHASAR (*entering*). My lord!

BASSANIO. Find Gratiano for me.

BALTHASAR. Here he comes, my lord!

[*Enter* GRATIANO, *followed by* ANTONIO.

BASSANIO. She has agreed. Nerissa and she have gone to robe themselves. Has Gratiano told you, Antonio, what we plan?

ANTONIO. He has, and I dislike it.

BASSANIO. That's no matter. What's next to do?

GRATIANO. Get Shylock here to listen to the play.

BASSANIO. Balthasar, go to Shylock's chamber and bid him come to us here.

GRATIANO. Tell him your mistress desires to speak to him.

BALTHASAR. I will, my lord, but Doctor Bellario is with him now.

BASSANIO. Doctor Bellario!

ANTONIO. I suspect your cousin, Bassanio, I suspect him. He is a lawyer, and all lawyers are suspectable.

BASSANIO (to BALTHASAR). Go and tell Shylock what I have bid you. (BALTHASAR goes out.) What can Bellario be saying to him now?

GRATIANO. Bassanio, be civil to the Jew when he arrives. Rude words and frowning looks will not prevail with him.

ANTONIO. But if Portia sees him here, she will not consent to play!

GRATIANO. There'll be no play. When he sees her, the sight will be sufficient. He'll go in dudgeon, and that's what Bassanio wants.

BASSANIO. We'll have some sport with this performance, Gratiano.

GRATIANO. And bait the Jew a second time.

ANTONIO. I do not like this game! . . . (He is about to go out.)

BASSANIO. Stay here with us, Antonio.

ANTONIO. I am not anxious to meet Shylock without a larger company.

BASSANIO. He will not harm you, man. Stand by. Gratiano, go and tell our guests what we propose and bring them here.

GRATIANO. They'll throng to it. (Exit.)

BASSANIO. I'll make myself the master of this house before the night is out. (Enter BALTHASAR.) Well, sir?

BALTHASAR. My lord, Shylock bids me say he is not well and begs to be excused! . . .

BASSANIO. Return and tell him we'll not detain him long. The matter is important.

BALTHASAR. I will, my lord, but his words were firm.

BASSANIO. Let yours be firmer. Stay! Was Doctor Bellario with him when you left?

BALTHASAR. Not now, my lord.

BASSANIO. Where is he, then?

BALTHASAR. I do not know, my lord.

BASSANIO. When you have brought Shylock here, go and find him.

BALTHASAR. Yes, my lord. (*Exit.*)

[GRATIANO, *followed by the guests, enters. There is a sound of talk and laughter mingled.* JESSICA *goes to* BASSANIO.]

JESSICA. What is it, Bassanio?

BASSANIO. A game, my dear!

JESSICA. I beg you, do not bait my father.

BASSANIO. There'll be no baiting. Stay here or go, which pleases you.

JESSICA. I'll go, my lord. I cannot stay and see him baited thus.

BASSANIO. Wait for me in the garden, near the gate. When this is done, I'll come to you. (*Exit* JESSICA.) (BASSANIO *joins the guests.*) Are you acquainted with our purpose?

A GENTLEMAN. Gratiano has told us of it.

A LADY. This will be the merriest masque of all.

ANTONIO. Indeed, I hope it will. I did not like it much when it was last performed.

BASSANIO. I pray you, gentles all, group yourselves about the room and leave the centre free.

GRATIANO. But where's the Jew?

BALTHASAR. I've sent for him. Are Portia and Nerissa ready?

A GENTLEMAN. I see them coming.

BASSANIO. Go, Gratiano, and bid them stay outside until we send for them. (GRATIANO *goes out.*) All you, my friends, have heard of how Antonio here, once a merchant in Venice, came near to losing his life! . . .

[*Murmurs of sarcastic assent.*

A YOUNG MAN. We have, indeed, Bassanio, and feel

sure we'll hear it many times again. (*The guests laugh with the young man.*)

ANTONIO (*to the young man*). You are an unmannerly youth ! . . .

BASSANIO. Antonio, please ! The Jew who sought our poor Antonio's flesh is here, within this house. (*Murmurs of astonishment.*) Bassanio's guest against Bassanio's will. But we've a plan to drive him hence and entertain us all. Sit here a while and you will see it.

[*The guests arrange themselves, chatting together, and as they do so,* BALTHASAR *returns.*]

BASSANIO. Well, Balthasar, what's Shylock's answer now ?

BALTHASAR. He's here, my lord.

[SHYLOCK *enters.*

SHYLOCK. You sent for me.

BASSANIO. My wife bids me say she has an entertainment for our guests and hopes you'll witness it.

SHYLOCK. I do not see her here.

BASSANIO. She is preparing for the play. Sit here and we'll begin.

SHYLOCK. I am not used to such entertainments, nor am I yet enough recovered to enjoy one. I beg you, make my excuse to her.

BASSANIO. She made particular request that you should see our play, and I, repenting of my conduct to you here to-day, now join my plea to hers.

SHYLOCK. I have no taste for mummery, my lord, but since it pleases her to bid me here, I'll stay.

BASSANIO. I thank you, Shylock. There is a quiet seat, close by that pillar. Sit there, and if your illness overcomes you, you can steal away unnoticed.

SHYLOCK. What is this play ?

BASSANIO. A little piece invented by my wife to entertain her guests. She thought of it a moment since, and said it would provide merriment for all of us, but most for you.

SHYLOCK. For me ?

BASSANIO. Those were her words. " 'Twill much amuse the Jew," she said. She had forgot, no doubt, you are a Christian now.

SHYLOCK. Were those her words?

BASSANIO. Exactly as I have repeated.

GRATIANO (*entering*). We're ready, my lord. May we begin?

BASSANIO. One moment. Doctor Bellario is not here. (*To* SHYLOCK.) Pray, seat yourself, sir.

[BALTHASAR *enters*.

BALTHASAR. My lord, Doctor Bellario begs you not to delay the entertainment. He is completing an instrument, and will come immediately he has it finished.

BASSANIO. Will that be long?

BALTHASAR. Not long, my lord.

BASSANIO (*to* SHYLOCK). We are holding a trial, Shylock. Antonio is the defendant.

SHYLOCK. Antonio defendant!

BASSANIO. It is a part with which he is familiar.

SHYLOCK. One moment, my lord! What is this entertainment to which I am bid so urgently?

BASSANIO. Restrain your curiosity, Shylock, for a moment more. Gratiano here is the plaintiff in a suit against Antonio.

SHYLOCK. Yes.

BASSANIO. A young judge has heard the case and will now give sentence. I pray you, resume your seat. (SHYLOCK, *with an appearance of reluctance, does so*.) Bid the young judge enter, Gratiano.

GRATIANO. Come in, O wise young judge!

[PORTIA, *wearing her lawyer's gown, enters, followed by* NERISSA *in her clerk's gown.* SHYLOCK *has his back to them—his face to the audience.*]

BASSANIO (*to* PORTIA). You're welcome, sir. Antonio and . . . Shylock, both stand forth.

[SHYLOCK *starts up from his seat, and* PORTIA *and he see each other.*]

SHYLOCK (*to* PORTIA). Who are you?

BASSANIO. Do you remember this upright judge, old Jew?

PORTIA. Oh, what a knavish trick is this!

SHYLOCK. Who are you? Are you a man or are you? . . .

PORTIA (*taking off her cap*). I am Portia, Bassanio's wife!

5

SHYLOCK. But in those robes ! . . . Are you my judge ?

PORTIA. I was your judge.

GRATIANO. An upright judge, Jew ; a Daniel, a Daniel come to judgment. O, Jew, do you remember now ?

SHYLOCK (to PORTIA). I did not know. I pray you, give me leave to go from hence.

[*Enter* DOCTOR BELLARIO.

PORTIA. A moment, sir, I beg. (*To* BELLARIO.) Cousin Bellario, was it by your design that this play-acting was done ?

BELLARIO. What play-acting ?

BASSANIO. 'Twas my design.

PORTIA. Yours ! My lord, I ask no more from you than this, that if there be gentility in you, you show some signs of it.

BASSANIO. I am your husband ! . . .

PORTIA. I'm glad you have remembered that, for I had near forgot it. But know, my lord, whether you be my husband or my harpy ! . . .

BASSANIO. Harpy !

BELLARIO. Cousin !

PORTIA. The word I used was " harpy." Whiche'er you be, my lord, I still am mistress of this house. You have insulted this old man ! . . .

BELLARIO. Insulted him !

PORTIA. And made me party to the insult, and I demand that you shall here before our guests apologize to him.

BASSANIO. Apologize !

BELLARIO. What has happened ? Will no one explain ?

BASSANIO. I'll see him dead and damned ere I apologize.

SHYLOCK. Madam, I am a stranger here and have no claim on your consideration. Presently, I shall be gone. I beg you, leave this quarrel with your husband.

PORTIA. Sir, I beg your pardon for the wrong you've suffered here to-night. What was done was not by my desire.

BASSANIO. But it was done with mine. Get out, you Jew !

PORTIA. Bassanio ! Leave my house !

[*There is consternation among the guests.*

BASSANIO. Leave this . . . house !

BELLARIO. Portia, your guests are troubled by their presence at this quarrel. (*To the Guests.*) My cousin will not feel aggrieved if you withdraw. (*Some of them move away.*)

PORTIA. I beg you not to go, until my husband has repaired the wrong he's done.

BELLARIO. Nay, please, all of you, go and leave us to settle this tedious dispute.

ANTONIO. Does that mean me?

BELLARIO. Yes, you especially.

BASSANIO. One moment, all! You've heard me ordered from my home because I do not choose to have this gentleman my guest. Well, since I'm ordered out, I'll go! . . .

BELLARIO. Bassanio, be reasonable! . . .

BASSANIO. Reasonable! I, a Christian gentleman, am banished by my wife that she may gratify a Jew who could not keep his faith! . . .

SHYLOCK. My faith!

BASSANIO. Who could not keep his faith, but went shivering to a Christian Church, lest he should lose his money or his life. There's a fine Jew for you! There's a faithful, upright, honest Jew.

SHYLOCK. O, this is excess of misery!

BASSANIO. I beg you, gentles, tell me what sort of Jew is he that changes his religion to save his skin. Would one of you deny the Christ to keep his little hoard of money and his life?

OMNES. No, no, no! We'd die first. The man's a traitor to his faith!

BASSANIO. Did not our fathers sweat in bloody war to keep their faith? And are not we, men and women, aye, and children too, ready to give our lives for it? (*Shouts of agreement.*) But what Jew will fight for his? What Jew will fight for anything? Has any Jew a country he will die for?

PORTIA. My lord, you have not died for yours!

BASSANIO. Peace, woman! I'll say what's in my mind. There is no Jew will fight. There is no country that a Jew will die for, and we see here how soon a Jew will change his faith if that will bring him profit and security. But is that all we Christians want? Are we poor, crawling things that must have comfort and protection, and will not fight when there is need to fight? Admit a Jew to equal rights and he will drag you down to bargaining and little plots of peace. (*Murmurs of assent from the company*.) Now, Jew, I have you on the hip! You that wore away the stones about the synagogue, to save a year or two of old, exhausted life, betrayed your race to be a Christian.

SHYLOCK. I had compulsion put on me.

BASSANIO. Compulsion! And what's compulsion to a man that loves his faith? I am no saint, as all of you can testify, but by my God I'd let myself be torn in shreds of bleeding flesh ere I'd renounce my faith or be compelled to one I loathed.

SHYLOCK. I will not stay with you. Let me go!

BASSANIO. False, faithless Jew!

SHYLOCK. I am not false. I keep my faith!

GRATIANO. How's this—you keep your faith?

ANTONIO. You swore in Venice, you would be a Christian. 'Twas I that made him do so.

BASSANIO. Come, Jew-Christian, Christian-Jew, what do you mean by this, this false but faithful, this treacherous truth, dishonourable honour?

PORTIA. Old man, I give you leave to go. Go now. They'll taunt you here to speech you may regret.

BASSANIO. Are you a Christian, Jew, or are you a Jew, Christian?

PORTIA. Do not answer him, but go.

BASSANIO. He shall not go. I charge you all, note what he says. This man is bound in law to be a Christian. His lands, his money and his life depend on it. You heard him say he was not false to Jewry. How is it, Shylock? Are you a Christian or a Jew?

SHYLOCK (*slowly*). I am a Christian! . . .

BASSANIO. By law or by desire?

PORTIA. He is not bound to answer you, Bassanio. Go, now, old gentleman!

BASSANIO. Gentleman! My lady wife calls this usurer a gentleman! Yet he is false to all his fathers' faith.

PORTIA. Come, Shylock! Come, away!

[*She leads him towards the door by which he entered.*

BASSANIO. False Jew! Renegade Jew! Christian Jew!

I pray you, all, note him as he goes, sneaking from our
just rebukes. This Jew that loved his faith was lightly
led from it ! For what ? Money ! A handful of ducats
won him from his race and his religion ! (*Laughter from
the guests.*) A false and faithless Jew, by God ! I pray
you, call him by his name : False Jew !

> [*There is a burst of mocking laughter, and then ascend-
> ing shouts of " False Jew ! False Jew ! " and
> " Traitor Jew ! " and " Judas ! Judas ! " The
> guests surge about* SHYLOCK, *taunting and deriding
> him. Some of them even jostle him.* PORTIA *breaks
> from the crowd, and* SHYLOCK *staggers after her.*]

PORTIA. My Lord !

BASSANIO. You call me, sweet wife ?

PORTIA. I beg of you, and you, my guests, that now
you leave my house !

BASSANIO. Have you turned Jewess, then ? Here's a
pretty Hebrew ! . . .

PORTIA. I am more faithful to my faith, Bassanio,
than you to me. I bid you go.

BASSANIO. I'll go. Good-night, old faithless Jew !
Good-night, you holy one of Israel. False Jew !

SHYLOCK. I am a Jew !

BASSANIO. You are a Jew ! By God, he changes
quick. He was a Christian a moment since.

SHYLOCK. I am a Jew. I keep our holy Sabbath in
my heart. By law, I am a Christian, made to kneel in
Christian church, but in my heart, beneath my Christian
cloak, I am a Jew ! . . .

> [*He throws off his rich garment and reveals his Jewish
> gaberdine.* PORTIA *and he are now dressed exactly
> as they were in the Court Scene of " The Merchant
> of Venice."*]

ANTONIO. The Duke of Venice shall hear of this ! I
warrant you, the Duke shall hear of this !

GRATIANO. Vile Jew, to mock our Christian faith !

BASSANIO. Here's a Jew, and a very pretty Jew, that's
neither fish, flesh, fowl nor good red herring ! Do you
eat pork, master Christian-Jew ?

PORTIA (*to* SHYLOCK). I am ashamed, sir, that you
have been so vilely treated in my house,

BASSANIO. Come gentles, let us go. This house will presently become a synagogue, and we, being Christians, will be foreign here. Gratiano, we'll continue our festival in your Christian home.

GRATIANO. We will, my lord. I'll warrant you there'll be no Jews in my house. Where is the wench with whom I danced?

A GIRL. I'm here, Gratiano.

GRATIANO (*embracing her*). You'll come and dance with me!

NERISSA. Husband! Gratiano!

GRATIANO. Puff! puff! old sourface!

BASSANIO. Come, then!

[BASSANIO *and* GRATIANO, *with the girl between them, go out, followed by the guests.* NERISSA, *baulked and angry, stands for a moment.*]

NERISSA (*aside*). I know what plans Bassanio has with Jessica. Lorenzo'll hear of this. (*Exit.*)

ANTONIO. I'm sorry, Portia! . . .

[*She does not answer, and, after a moment of bewilderment, he goes out too.*]

BELLARIO. This is a distressing matter. Your husband is an obstinate, but eloquent man, Portia. I had arranged with Shylock here that he should lend you money! . . .

PORTIA. Lend me money!

BELLARIO. Yes, and very reasonably, too.

PORTIA. O, I am humiliated! (*To* SHYLOCK.) Sir, what can I say to you?

SHYLOCK. Nothing! Say nothing! There is nothing to say. I pray you, send for your husband and make peace with him. I'll leave you now. There is a fellow here will take me to my daughter's house, and when that's done, I'll go to Venice. You will not see me again. Make peace, then, with your husband.

PORTIA. Good-night, Shylock!

SHYLOCK. Good-night, Portia!

[*He picks up his cloak and goes out*

THE FOURTH ACT

A bedroom in the house of LORENZO *and* JESSICA. *There is a wide window at the back of the scene, overlooking the garden. On the spectator's right is a narrow door, near the front of the scene, which leads along a short passage to the room where* LORENZO *and* JESSICA'S *children sleep. On the spectator's left, in the middle of the wall, is a larger door leading to th rest of the house.*

[*The scene is in darkness, except for moonlight, when the curtain rises, but almost immediately* LAUNCELOT GOBBO, *carrying a lamp and followed by* SHYLOCK, *enters.*]

GOBBO.   This is their room, sir !

SHYLOCK.   Where are my grandsons ?

GOBBO.   Hush, sir ! Do not speak so loud. (*He points to the small door.*) They are in that room. There is a little passage which leads to it. . . .

SHYLOCK (*interrupting him*).   Let us go into it quickly, then !

GOBBO.   Stay, sir ! I'll go first and see if they are asleep.

[*He opens the little door and goes through the passage to the room where the children are.* SHYLOCK *stands in silence until he returns.*]

GOBBO.   They are asleep.   I listened to their breathing. Come, sir, but be quiet, if you please, lest they wake.

SHYLOCK.   And why should they not wake ? May a man not speak with his grandsons ?

GOBBO.   Nay, sir, if you will not behave with discretion, I will not let you go to them at all.   You must promise that you will not wake them nor speak to them, or I will have no more to do with the matter. If lord Lorenzo were to know I'd brought you here, he'd make a very fine example of me.

SHYLOCK. Well, then, I promise.

[*But before they can enter the children's room,* YOUNG LORENZO, *a boy about nine years old, enters, wearing his bedclothes.*]

YOUNG LORENZO. Launcelot Gobbo!

GOBBO. You are asleep, young master! I do assure you, you are asleep and dreaming!

YOUNG LORENZO. I heard a noise. Who is that old man with you?

GOBBO. An old gentleman! Just an old gentleman!

LORENZO. I do not know him. Who is he?

GOBBO. An old gentleman, master Lorenzo!

YOUNG LORENZO (*going to* SHYLOCK). Who are you?

SHYLOCK. I am one that loved your mother, child!

YOUNG LORENZO. Did she love you?

SHYLOCK. I thought so.

YOUNG LORENZO. Then I expect she did. Mother always loves people who love her. Have you come to stay with us?

GOBBO. Oh, no, master Lorenzo. The old gentleman is just looking round, and you must not tell anyone that he's been here.

YOUNG LORENZO. Why?

GOBBO. It would upset your father to hear that anyone had been here but him.

YOUNG LORENZO (to SHYLOCK). Do you know my father?

SHYLOCK. I have seen him.

YOUNG LORENZO. His name is Lorenzo. So is mine. What is your name, old gentleman?

GOBBO. Oh, sir, I beg! . . .

SHYLOCK (*disregarding* GOBBO). Shylock!

YOUNG LORENZO. Shylock! What a funny name!

SHYLOCK. Have you never heard it before?

YOUNG LORENZO. No. I suppose it is a foreign name. Why have you come here? My father's gone to France, and my mother is at Portia's party!

SHYLOCK. I came to see you, my dear.

YOUNG LORENZO. Me! Won't you sit down?

SHYLOCK (*seating himself*). You and your brothers!

YOUNG LORENZO. Do you know us, then?

SHYLOCK. I have heard of you. Let me look at you, my dear!

> [*He lifts the child on to his knee and regards him very closely.*]

YOUNG LORENZO. Do you think I am handsome?

SHYLOCK. Yes. You remind me of my wife.

YOUNG LORENZO. How funny! Are my brothers like your wife?

SHYLOCK. I do not know. I have never seen them.

YOUNG LORENZO. Oh, I'll show them to you. (*Comes off* SHYLOCK'S *knee.*) But they're asleep. You must be very quiet. You see, I am older than they are, so I don't go to sleep as soon as they do. You'll be quiet, won't you?

SHYLOCK. Yes!

YOUNG LORENZO. Promise!

SHYLOCK. I promise!

YOUNG LORENZO. Bring the lamp! (SHYLOCK *does so.*) Take my hand and I'll lead you to them.

GOBBO (*in distress*). O, young master Lorenzo! . . . (*To* SHYLOCK.) Sir! . . .

YOUNG LORENZO. Hush, Gobbo! Hush! You have no control over your tongue. (*To* SHYLOCK.) That's what father says about him. Now, gently, tiptoe, tiptoe! . . .

> [YOUNG LORENZO *leads* SHYLOCK *into the passage. The door remains open. The room is now moonlit only.*]

GOBBO (*alone*). Here's a packet of trouble! I wish I had never consented to bring old master Jew here! That brat'll blab about him to my lord and I shall be disgraced. (*He goes to the door by which he and* SHYLOCK *entered the room, and listens. Then he goes to the open door of the children's room.*) Good master Shylock, I beg you, dispatch and be quick. Someone will come! . . .

> [YOUNG LORENZO *comes to the door.*

YOUNG LORENZO. Go away, Gobbo! You mustn't interrupt us. Go away!

> [*He shuts the door, leaving* GOBBO *alone in the bedroom,*

GOBBO. O, miserable Gobbo! Miserable, miserable Gobbo! This is what comes of being kind. I may as well hang myself now or marry the fat innkeeper, for I'll get a poor greeting from my lord when he hears of this. I'll go! I'll not wait! I'll spend the night with friends and say I ne'er came home at all, and if the brat blabs to his father, I'll swear he dreamt it all. I'll get so drunk that I'll have a hundred witnesses to prove I was not here to-night. Farewell, Jew! Farewell, Christians that should be Jews! Farewell, everything! And now I'll go and souse myself!

[*He goes out. The door of the children's chamber opens, and* SHYLOCK, *carrying the light, reappears.*]

SHYLOCK. Gobbo! (*He comes into the centre of the room.*) Gobbo!

[YOUNG LORENZO *appears in the doorway.*

YOUNG LORENZO. Where's Gobbo?

SHYLOCK. I think he must have gone. (*He puts the lamp down and seats himself.*) Come, here, Lorenzo!

[*The boy climbs on to his knee again.*

YOUNG LORENZO. Why did Gobbo go? It's so funny to leave me alone with a stranger!

SHYLOCK. A stranger!

YOUNG LORENZO. Yes. You're a stranger!

SHYLOCK. I'm a stranger! Tell me, Lorenzo, has no one ever told you about your grandfather?

YOUNG LORENZO. Oh, yes! He's dead!

SHYLOCK. Dead! Who is dead?

YOUNG LORENZO. My grandfather! His name was Lorenzo, too!

SHYLOCK. Oh, that grandfather!

YOUNG LORENZO. We are the three Lorenzos: my grandfather, my father, and me!

SHYLOCK. But you have another one, your mother's father?

YOUNG LORENZO. Oh, yes, but he lives a long way off. He's a foreigner, not quite like us!

SHYLOCK. And you never see him?

YOUNG LORENZO. No.

SHYLOCK. Do you never wish to see him?

YOUNG LORENZO. Father and mother do not like to speak about him.

SHYLOCK. Why?

YOUNG LORENZO. I don't know. What a funny old man you are! You keep on asking questions.

SHYLOCK. Don't you ever think of your other grandfather?

YOUNG LORENZO. Sometimes. Not often. Do you know, Launcelot Gobbo told me once that my other grandfather is a Jew!

SHYLOCK. Did he? And what did you say to that?

YOUNG LORENZO. I hit him with my whip, and then I told my father what he had said, and father was very angry and beat him again. He got two beatings for that. Of course, poor Gobbo was drunk, but he ought not to have said such a thing.

SHYLOCK. Why, my dear?

YOUNG LORENZO. Well, would you like to be told that your grandfather was a Jew, even if you'd never seen him?

SHYLOCK. My grandfather was a Jew.

YOUNG LORENZO. Oh! Then you are a Jew?

SHYLOCK. I am . . . a sort of a Jew.

YOUNG LORENZO. But I thought all Jews were wicked people. You're kind.

SHYLOCK. Do you like me, Lorenzo?

YOUNG LORENZO. I think so. Yes, I do.

[SHYLOCK *hugs the boy to him, and there is silence for a moment or two.*]

YOUNG LORENZO. I'm so sleepy now.

SHYLOCK. Are you? Shall I take you back to bed?

YOUNG LORENZO. Will you tell me a story first?

SHYLOCK. I do not know many stories.

YOUNG LORENZO. Gobbo knows a lot. (*He yawns.*) Oh, dear, I'm so tired!

SHYLOCK. Lie close to me! . . .

[*The boy snuggles down into* SHYLOCK'S *arms, making little childish noises of content as he does so.*]

YOUNG LORENZO (*in a sleepy voice*). Go on! Tell me a story!

SHYLOCK. There was once an old man . . .

YOUNG LORENZO. Yes.

SHYLOCK. Who was very lonely. And he started off one day on a journey . . .

YOUNG LORENZO. Was it a long journey?

SHYLOCK. A very long journey. He wanted to find someone he loved and to see some little children that he had never seen! . . .

YOUNG LORENZO. Yes.

SHYLOCK. And when he had travelled a long while he came to a place where he found a little boy . . .

YOUNG LORENZO. Like me?

SHYLOCK. Just like you!

YOUNG LORENZO. It isn't a very amusing story!

SHYLOCK. No, no, it isn't an amusing story!

YOUNG LORENZO. Don't you know anything funny or exciting?

SHYLOCK. I'll try and think of something.

YOUNG LORENZO. I'll keep quiet while you think. Shall I?

SHYLOCK. Yes. Do.

> [*They are silent for a moment or two. Then* SHYLOCK *sees that the boy is asleep. He gathers him up in his arms and carries him very gently to the children's bedroom.*
>
> *After a few moments, the outer door opens, and* JESSICA *enters. She glances around the room and sees that the children's door is open. She goes to it, listens a moment, but hears nothing. She shuts the door and goes to the window, which she opens, and leans out.*]

JESSICA. Bassanio!

BASSANIO (*in the garden*). Jessica!

JESSICA. Hush! All's quiet, but make no noise!

BASSANIO. I'll climb this way!

JESSICA. Take care, my lord!

BASSANIO. This is a trifle, Jessica, to me.

> [*She moves to the side of the window, and as she does so,* BASSANIO *appears.*]

JESSICA. Oh, my lord!

> [BASSANIO *swings himself over the sill into the room.*

BASSANIO. Why, what's ado?

JESSICA. I was afraid you'd fall.

BASSANIO. Fall! My dear, I've often done this before. Come!

[He takes her in his arms and embraces her.

BASSANIO. Little blackbird!

JESSICA. Do you truly love me, Bassanio?

BASSANIO. Truly I do. (*Kissing her.*) Little blackbird! I love your deep, dark hair! . . .

JESSICA. Portia has golden hair.

BASSANIO. She has. I loved it once.

JESSICA. You do not love it now?

BASSANIO. How can a man love anything continuously? Kiss me!

[He pulls her to him and kisses her.

JESSICA. Will you not love me continuously?

BASSANIO. I'll love you as long as I can. No one can promise more. An active gentleman that has his health and strength, when there are no wars, must have variety of love. I'll not pretend, Jessica, that I will always be faithful to you, for that's impossible, but I'll be faithful to you as long as I can! I have loved fair women and dark women and tall women and little women, and women that were fierce and women that were gentle, but I have never loved one woman only. I have a wide heart, Jessica, with room for many sorts of women.

JESSICA. I'd have you love me only.

BASSANIO. They all say that. But what an arrogance it is to deem yourself so high above all others that there's no thought left for anyone but you? I do not think myself unique. Then why do you think you're unique?

JESSICA. Will you be tolerant then if Portia takes a lover?

BASSANIO. No, by God! But I'm a man, and she's a woman.

JESSICA. I am a woman, and Lorenzo is a man.

BASSANIO. No, Lorenzo's a poet. Besides, all logic breaks down somewhere. Mine breaks down here. I'll take another's wife, but heaven help him that takes mine.

JESSICA. I care not, so that you love me.

BASSANIO. I do.

JESSICA. Then take me! . . .

[*The door of the children's chamber opens and* SHYLOCK *enters.*]

BASSANIO. Good God, what's that?

JESSICA. My father!

BASSANIO. God's blood, the everlasting Jew!

[SHYLOCK *comes close to them.*

SHYLOCK. I hardly thought to find you here, my lord!

BASSANIO. Your presence surprises me as much as mine surprises you. Did you arrange this, Jessica?

JESSICA. No, my lord! Father, how came you here?

SHYLOCK. I had a longing to see my grandsons, and while you danced Gobbo brought me here.

JESSICA. Gobbo!

BASSANIO. I'll kill Gobbo.

SHYLOCK. Your sons are sleeping, Jessica.

JESSICA. Did you speak to them?

SHYLOCK. I spoke to young Lorenzo. He does not know who I am. I'll go now, and perhaps Bassanio will conduct me to an inn.

BASSANIO. I'll not conduct you! . . .

SHYLOCK. It would be unmannerly of me to leave you with my daughter when her husband is not here.

BASSANIO. I'll pardon the unmannerliness.

SHYLOCK. But yet I cannot go unless you do me honour and come with me.

BASSANIO. I do not walk with Jews! . . .

SHYLOCK. My daughter is a Jewess.

BASSANIO. Much is forgiven to women.

SHYLOCK. You hate Jews?

BASSANIO. Like Hell!

SHYLOCK. Do you hate Hell? And take so little care to keep out of it?

BASSANIO. I am not in a mood for pleasantries. I beg you, take your leave.

SHYLOCK. While you remain here? My lord, though I'm a Jew, I have a father's heart. Jessica, I gave you all the love my heart could hold, and you betrayed me for a man that hated me. Now, I find you betraying him!

BASSANIO. Come, come! . . .

SHYLOCK. Silence, my lord. I am this woman's father. There is a legend of our race that wives and husbands shall be faithful to each other, whatever comes to them, and I have always held it dear. You have despised me for my race, and I have borne your contempt as best I could. But here's a different cause, my lord. I love my daughter, though she loves me not, and hold her faithfulness and honour as a trust, although her husband keeps my name concealed from her children's ears. And so I bid you, lord Bassanio, leave this house.

BASSANIO. You bid me ! . . .

SHYLOCK. I bid you leave this house, and leave it now.

BASSANIO. I'll see you damned, and damned again ! . . .

[*A single loud knock is heard on the street door.*

JESSICA. Hush ! What's that ?

[*They remain silent. The knock is repeated.* JESSICA *hesitates. Then she goes towards the door.*]

JESSICA. I pray you go, my lord, and you, father, go, too.

BASSANIO. Why, what's to do ? We can conceal ourselves, if there is need.

JESSICA. If it should be Lorenzo ! . . .

BASSANIO. But he's in France, or thereabouts !

JESSICA. I fear this knocking bodes no good. I beg you, dear Bassanio, go.

SHYLOCK. How shall I depart ?

JESSICA. There's no way now but by the window.

SHYLOCK. I am not skilled in window-work.

[*The knock is heard for the third time.*

JESSICA. He knocks again. I beg you, go ! . . .

BASSANIO. If there is need, we'll hide ourselves. Go now and see who 'tis.

[JESSICA *goes out.*

BASSANIO. The hour is late for visitors.

SHYLOCK You did not find it so, my lord.

BASSANIO. My visit, good Jew, was not a ceremonial one. However, I am not here to bandy jokes with you.

SHYLOCK. I suspected that, my lord.

BASSANIO. Be silent a moment. (*He listens at the door.*)

SHYLOCK. What do you hear ?

BASSANIO. What can I hear with you chattering ? . . . (*He listens hard and hears the voice of* PORTIA.) My God, my wife !

SHYLOCK. Who ?

BASSANIO. Portia! My wife! (*He listens again.*) And Lorenzo! Lorenzo's with her! They must not find me here!

> [*He hurries towards the window.*

SHYLOCK. Lorenzo!

BASSANIO. He hates Jews more than I do. (*Looking out.*) God, there's someone in the garden! (*He comes into the room again, and goes to the outer door.*) They are coming here. What room is that?

SHYLOCK. A passage that leads to where my grandsons sleep.

BASSANIO. We'll hide there!

SHYLOCK. Why should I hide? And from whom?

BASSANIO. Lorenzo, fool! How will he treat Jessica if he finds you here? Come, hide, Jew, with me!

> [*He goes into the passage, leaving* SHYLOCK *alone in the room. The sound of* JESSICA'S *voice in expostulation grows louder and nearer, and* LORENZO *is heard in hot reply.*]

BASSANIO (*peering out of the passage*). Come, Shylock, quickly!

> [SHYLOCK *stands for a moment. Then he follows* BASSANIO *into the passage and shuts the door behind him. The room is empty for a moment. Then* PORTIA, *followed by* JESSICA, *enters.*]

JESSICA. This is intolerable, madam. (*Lorenzo enters, and* JESSICA *turns on him.*) How can you permit this outrage on your wife?

LORENZO. I have my cause for these suspicions.

PORTIA. There's no one here.

JESSICA. I told you so. That I should live to be insulted in my own room by my own husband, and you, madam!

LORENZO. What man was here to-night?

JESSICA. No man, I swear!

PORTIA. Was not Bassanio here, my husband?

JESSICA. Bassanio! In my room?

LORENZO. Aye, or in your bed. Let's be blunt, madam! There's no occasion here for delicate conversation!

JESSICA. I won't answer these outrageous insults!

PORTIA. I demand an answer, Jessica. Rumour has

joined Bassanio's name with yours, and not lightly either. Once more, I ask you, was my husband here to-night ?

JESSICA. No, nor was he ever here. I am ashamed, my lady, that you should put such questions to me, but I am more ashamed that my husband lets you put them.

LORENZO. You do not love Bassanio ?

JESSICA. No.

PORTIA. Nor ever entertained a loving thought of him ?

JESSICA. No more than is my duty to my husband's friend.

PORTIA. Then we have wronged you ?

JESSICA. Deeply. Unforgivably.

        [LORENZO *goes to the window and leans out*

LORENZO. Balthasar !

BALTHASAR (*from the garden*). Yes, my lord !

LORENZO. Have you got Gobbo there ?

BALTHASAR. He's here, my lord !

LORENZO. Listen, Gobbo ! What person came with you to-night ?

GOBBO (*in a whining voice*). No one, my lord.

LORENZO. Liar ! Beat him, Balthasar !

BALTHASAR. I will, my lord.

    [GOBBO'S *cries of pain are heard as* BALTHASAR *beats him.*]

LORENZO. Now, rascal, will you answer ?

GOBBO. I brought no one, my lord. O, dear lord Lorenzo, let me be, I pray you.

LORENZO. Have you seen aught, Balthasar, since you came here ?

BALTHASAR. One came to the window a while since, my lord.

LORENZO. Who was it ?

BALTHASAR. I could not see.

LORENZO (*turning to* PORTIA *and* JESSICA). Then some-one was here. Balthasar saw a figure at this window.

JESSICA. I went to the window, my lord.

LORENZO (*to* BALTHASAR). Was it the lady Jessica you saw ?

BALTHASAR. No, my lord !

JESSICA. How can he tell ?

LORENZO. Who was it then?

BALTHASAR. I think it was a man.

LORENZO (*slamming the window to*). Hell and damnation! (*Coming into the room.*) You had best be honest, madam. Who was it came?

JESSICA. My lord, you do me wrong. 'Twas no one, that I swear!

PORTIA. What became of the man Balthasar saw at the window? Did he escape?

LORENZO. I had forgot that. (*He goes to the window again.*) Balthasar!

BALTHASAR. My lord!

LORENZO. Did this man you saw at the window leave by it?

BALTHASAR. No, my lord.

LORENZO. Then he's still here!

JESSICA. No, no, my lord, he's not.

PORTIA. Then he *was* here?

JESSICA. No, no, I do not mean that he was here. You put confusion in my mouth. Lorenzo, husband, no one was here, no one's here now. I swear it that am your loving wife.

PORTIA (*pointing to the door that leads to the children's room*). What door is that?

JESSICA. My children's room.

PORTIA. He may be there.

JESSICA (*interrupting them*). My children are asleep. You'll frighten them as you have frightened me.

LORENZO. Stand aside.

JESSICA (*kneeling before him and clasping him round the knees*). My lord Lorenzo, if you have ever loved me, trust me now, I beg you.

LORENZO. I'll trust no more. Give me leave.

JESSICA. I will not let you go! . . .

LORENZO. Then must I make you! . . .

[*He throws her aside and she falls heavily on the floor. His sword is out, and he makes a step towards the door. As he does so, it opens and* SHYLOCK *enters.*]

LORENZO. Shylock!

SHYLOCK. Lorenzo!

PORTIA. You!

SHYLOCK. My lady!

LORENZO. What means this? (*To* JESSICA.) How comes the Jew here?

SHYLOCK. I am her father, and hearing she had children, I had a wish to see them.

JESSICA. I did not bring him here, Lorenzo.

SHYLOCK. No, she did not bring me. I came against her will, without her knowledge. When she returned from Portia's house, she found me here, and while she was rebuking me, you came. Her heart's a timorous one, and when she heard the knocking at your door she was afraid 'twas you returning, and lest you might be angry with her for harbouring me, her father, and letting me see your children, my grandsons, she begged me to conceal myself. And so I did.

LORENZO. And you were here alone with her?

SHYLOCK. I was.

PORTIA. Was not my husband here?

SHYLOCK. No.

LORENZO. Oh, Jessica! (*He lifts her from the floor and holds her in his arms.*) I have wronged you deeply, Jessica.

[*She does not answer, but weeps lavishly on his breast while he comforts her.*]

SHYLOCK. A daughter's heart's a tender thing, Lorenzo. Affection for her father, despised of you, brought her to this. Use her kindly.

PORTIA. I've done you wrong, Jessica. I beg you'll pardon me.

LORENZO. Look up, my love!

JESSICA. It's hard, my lady, but I do forgive you.

PORTIA. I'll leave you now. Lorenzo, will you conduct me to the street?

LORENZO. I'll bid Balthasar meet you at the door (*He goes to the window and calls to* BALTHASAR.)

BALTHASAR. My lord!

LORENZO. Go to the front of the house and meet your mistress there. All's well here!

BALTHASAR. What shall I do with Gobbo, my lord?

LORENZO. Let him go, and bid him not come near this house again. (*He shuts the window.*) I am glad for

you, Portia, as much as for myself, that this night has
ended happily.

PORTIA. Yes. Thank you, Lorenzo!

LORENZO. Send graciously for Bassanio and bid him
home again.

PORTIA. Yes.

> [LORENZO *and she go out.   Immediately they have gone*
> JESSICA *sits up, her whole manner changed.*]

JESSICA (*to her father*). Where is he?

SHYLOCK. In there.

> [*She goes to the door and opens it.*

JESSICA. My lord! Come quickly.

> [BASSANIO *enters.*

BASSANIO. My God, what an escape!

JESSICA. Go, go!

BASSANIO. Is Balthasar there?

JESSICA (*at the window*). No.

BASSANIO (*to* SHYLOCK). Thanks, old Jew! Good-
night!

> [BASSANIO *puts his leg over the sill of the window.*

BASSANIO (*whispering to* JESSICA). I'll come again,
sweet chuck, some other night!

> [*He is about to drop from the window, when* PORTIA
> *returns.*]

PORTIA. I came to say! . . . (*Sees* BASSANIO, *who
disappears without realising that she has seen him.*) What
does this mean?

SHYLOCK. My lady, do not speak, I beg. This jade
will never harm you any more. I'll take good care of that.
But in your charity, let this pass.

PORTIA. Why did you deny that he was here?

SHYLOCK. I thought to save you pain.

PORTIA. Me! Pain! Why should you save me pain?

SHYLOCK. I do not know, except that you are kind.
I am old, and kindness has been rare in my life.

PORTIA. I thank you, sir, for your consideration. I
came to say " Good-night! " and wish you well.

SHYLOCK. Madam, I wish you well.

> [*Enter* LORENZO.

LORENZO. Balthasar is waiting at the door.

PORTIA. Thank you, Lorenzo. Good-night!

LORENZO. I'll come with you.

PORTIA. No need. Remain with Jessica. Her wounded heart needs comforting. And this old man, your father, dear Lorenzo, I commend him to your affection, for I have seldom known a more honourable gentleman.

[She goes out.

THE FIFTH ACT

The scene is laid in PORTIA'S *garden. The time is the next morning, and the garden is bright and sunny and full of flowers.* PORTIA *is sitting under a tree, apparently reading a book, but in reality she is listening to* STEPHANO *who, invisible to the audience as yet, is singing somewhere near at hand a song which he learned from his father. It is:*

> Tell me where is fancy bred,
>> Or in the heart or in the head?
> How begot, how nourished?
>> Reply, reply.
> It is engendered in the eyes,
> With gazing fed; and fancy dies
> In the cradle where it lies.
>> Let us all ring fancy's knell;
>> I'll begin it, Ding, dong, bell.

[He enters, his arms full of flowers and green stuff, as he sings the last two lines.]

PORTIA. Stephano!

STEPHANO. My lady!

PORTIA. Who taught you that song?

STEPHANO. My father, madam, when he was your servant.

PORTIA. I remember. He sang it when Bassanio came to choose the caskets.

STEPHANO. These flowers are for your chamber, my lady. I gathered them myself.

PORTIA. Thank you, Stephano.

STEPHANO. I'll take them to the house now.

PORTIA. Do.

[*He goes out, and as he goes he is heard singing, " Tell me where is fancy bred ! " The sound of his singing dies away.* PORTIA *sits back in her seat, but does not read. She is thinking of what happened in* JESSICA'S *bedroom last night.* BALTHASAR *enters.*]

BALTHASAR. My lady ! . . .

PORTIA (*interrupting him*). Has your lord returned ?

BALTHASAR. I have not seen him, my lady.

PORTIA. I thought perhaps he had returned. Well ?

BALTHASAR. Lord Lorenzo and his lady and the old gentleman from Venice ! . . .

PORTIA. Shylock ?

BALTHASAR. Yes, my lady ! They are within the house and wish to speak to you.

PORTIA. Bring them here.

BALTHASAR. I will, my lady !

[*He goes out. Hardly has he done so when* BASSANIO, *still unaware that Portia saw him drop from* JESSICA'S *window, enters by the same way that* STEPHANO *came.*]

BASSANIO. Portia !

PORTIA. You have returned, my lord !

BASSANIO. Yes. I learned an hour ago that after I had gone you sent the Jew fellow packing, and so I have returned, willing to forgive and to forget.

PORTIA. I am obliged to you, my lord !

BASSANIO. We'll say no more about it.

PORTIA. That, perhaps, will be best.

BASSANIO. Provided that the Jew does not return ! . . .

PORTIA. I'm afraid he's here already !

BASSANIO. What ! Again ?

PORTIA. Balthasar has just told me of his arrival. I'm waiting for him now.

BASSANIO. The fellow will take possession of the house if we're not careful. You must tell him to go ! . . .

PORTIA. I'm afraid that's not possible, my lord !

BASSANIO. Now, look here, Portia, once and for all this question of authority must be settled. A house which is divided against itself must fall.

PORTIA. My dear, you've been reading the Scriptures.

BASSANIO. I dislike irony, Portia. Please do not use it in my presence. There must be a head in every house. That's common sense, whether it is in the Scriptures or not, and the question is, Am I the head of this house or am I not?

PORTIA. I'm afraid you're not.

BASSANIO. Have I forgiven you for this?

PORTIA. You have. Shylock is now approaching, and with him are Jessica and Lorenzo.

BASSANIO (*startled*). Jessica! Lorenzo!

PORTIA. Yes. He is their father.

BASSANIO. Why have they come?

PORTIA. I do not know. To pay a visit, I suppose.

[BASSANIO, *baffled and bewildered, thinks for a moment. Then he turns on* PORTIA *angrily*.]

BASSANIO. I will not have this Jew man here! . . .

PORTIA (*rising from her seat*). He's here now!

[*For she has seen* BALTHASAR, *followed by* JESSICA, LORENZO, *and* SHYLOCK, *approaching from the house. She goes to greet them as they enter.*]

BASSANIO. The whole damned tribe are here.

BALTHASAR. Here is my lady!

PORTIA (*to* SHYLOCK). You wish to speak to me, Shylock?

[*Exit* BALTHASAR.

SHYLOCK. I do.

PORTIA. My husband's here!

SHYLOCK. What I've to say is his affair as much as yours.

BASSANIO. Can anything that concerns you interest or concern me?

SHYLOCK. Many things that concern me, sir, have interested you exceedingly. My daughter! . . .

BASSANIO. Does not interest me.

SHYLOCK. I thought she was your friend. I thought my son, Lorenzo, was your friend. Am I mistaken?

PORTIA. No, no, Shylock, you are not mistaken. Forgive my husband! (*A movement from* BASSANIO, *but she hurries on*.) He is out of temper. Last night, as you remember, we quarrelled, and since that time he has been away, wandering.

BASSANIO. Wandering, madam!

PORTIA. Roving, perhaps, is the word. He's tired, I fear, and not fit company for you.

BASSANIO. I'm fit enough for any company, but when a pack of Jews! . . .

LORENZO. My lord, you were not wont to speak to me like this. And Jessica, my wife . . .

BASSANIO. I speak as I am in the mood to speak.

LORENZO. You'll speak to me with some civility.

PORTIA. Peace, peace, gentlemen. This is not the time of day for bickering.

LORENZO. My wife complains, my lord, that you have sometimes troubled her with your attentions . . .

BASSANIO. I've troubled her! . . .

JESSICA. Too often you have troubled me, but I've resisted!

BASSANIO. This is a plot! . . .

PORTIA. Peace, peace! Lorenzo, Jessica, do you not know my lord? He has a catholic heart, but there's no harm in it. His tongue turns to admiration for a lady as sunflowers turn to light. That's all, Bassanio, is it not?

BASSANIO. There's some humour here.

PORTIA. None, Bassanio.

BASSANIO. I'll stay to hear no more.

PORTIA. But wait, Bassanio! I have not told you of a strange adventure that we had last night.

BASSANIO. Adventure, madam! At your age?

PORTIA. Yes, at my age. But not the kind you're thinking on. Last night, my lord, Lorenzo came hurrying home from France! . . .

LORENZO. I had not got so far as France, but only to the Venetian tavern a mile or two away from Belmont.

PORTIA. As you say, Lorenzo. Someone sent a message after him to say that Jessica, our sweet, obedient Jessica, was unfaithful to her husband.

JESSICA (weeping). A wicked, shameful lie!

BASSANIO. Jessica! Unfaithful! With whom?

PORTIA. With you, my lord!

BASSANIO. Me! By God's blood! . . .

LORENZO. I need not tell you, Bassanio, that I do not believe a word of it, despite your attempts! . . .

BASSANIO. Attempts! What attempts? Who has told this calumny of me? Was it this Jew here? . . .

SHYLOCK. You forget, my lord, that I came to Belmont yesterday after he had gone, and was too much occupied with your attentions to me to think about my son-in-law.

PORTIA. Poor Jessica is all a blur of tears. I fear our talk distresses her. When innocence is wronged, the hurt is deeper than when guilt's discovered. Do we annoy you, Jessica, with all this flippant talk?

JESSICA. I would rather not hear it.

PORTIA. Your desire is natural. But, Bassanio has not heard all, and since he's concerned as much as you, he ought to know the whole story. That's fair and just, is it not, Jessica? (*A sob from* JESSICA.) But I'll be brief. Listen, Bassanio! Lorenzo hurried here and told his story to me, after you had left last night, and I, to humour him, for, indeed, I did not doubt you, my lord, went with him to his house, where we found Jessica alone.

BASSANIO. Then I was not there?

PORTIA. No, you were not visible; I mean you were not there.

BASSANIO. Ha! Well, you must have frightened Jessica with your rude suspicions! What did you do, Jessica?

JESSICA. I wept.

PORTIA. That was right. We should always weep when we are doubted.

BASSANIO. You used her ill, Lorenzo.

LORENZO. I know, and am ashamed to think of it. (*He embraces* JESSICA.)

PORTIA. But listen to what follows, my lord. There *was* a man in Jessica's room.

BASSANIO. Was! . . .

PORTIA. Balthasar saw him. Balthasar's eyes are strong.

BASSANIO. Balthasar!

PORTIA. Our steward! You remember our steward, my lord? He saw the man and can identify him.

BASSANIO. Oh! Who was the man?

PORTIA. Can you not guess?

BASSANIO. How can I guess? I do not know what men frequent her room?

LORENZO. Bassanio!

PORTIA. A joke, Lorenzo. A poor joke, but his own! It is an easy thing to guess, Bassanio. What man should be in her room?

BASSANIO. Lorenzo!

PORTIA. Well answered! Well answered, Bassanio! Yet it was not her husband. Come, guess, my lord!

BASSANIO. I am not good at riddles. Who was it?

PORTIA. Why, her father! Shylock!

SHYLOCK. It was, my lord!

PORTIA. Is that not funny, Bassanio? We went to find a lover in her room, and found a grandfather tendering his grandsons!

BASSANIO. Ha! Ha, ha, ha!

PORTIA. It is funny, is it not, Bassanio?

BASSANIO (*more confident now*). Oh, very funny, very funny! Ha, ha, ha! Eh, Lorenzo, is this not a comical tale? You went out to be a cuckold and found yourself a son-in-law! . . .

PORTIA. That was much more satisfactory, wasn't it, Bassanio?

BASSANIO. By God, yes! Ha, ha, ha! Come, old Jew, you must see the humour of that.

SHYLOCK. Yes, I think I see it.

BASSANIO. Well, why don't you laugh, then? You know, Shylock, a Jew can't see a joke. Your race is too literal! That's what's the matter with it. You took the Old Testament much too seriously, Shylock, and that's why you lost the New one. Portia told me that, and it's true. You were all so busy looking for a common king to come and rule over you, that you didn't notice God, and that's an oversight that's going to cost you dear. Here, Jessica, come and confide in me! Was there not a lover in the cupboard all the time?

JESSICA. O, my lord!

LORENZO. Bassanio, this is unworthy of you!

BASSANIO. Come, come, Lorenzo, let's have our jest out! What, Jessica?

JESSICA. No, Bassanio, there was no one in the room but my father!

BASSANIO. No gallant gentleman, like me, to whisper endearments to you while Lorenzo went abroad?

JESSICA. My lord, I cannot bear to hear you speak like this.

LORENZO. Nor I. I think your jests, Bassanio, are in very poor taste. (*To* JESSICA.) I am ashamed to think that by my conduct last night I have subjected you to such insinuations.

BASSANIO. Well, well, the matter has ended happily. What brings you here this morning?

SHYLOCK. We've come to take our leave.

PORTIA. Your leave!

BASSANIO. What, all of you?

SHYLOCK. My daughter and her husband return with me to Venice to-day. Their servants will sell their house and follow when all is done.

BASSANIO. But, Lorenzo! . . .

LORENZO. I have a longing to live in Venice again, Bassanio. I dream of moonlit nights when Jessica and I can drift down the lagoons and listen to music. I'll sing to her sometimes or say my verses to her in the dusk! . . .

BASSANIO. H'm, that'll please her! Are you content to go to Venice, Jessica?

JESSICA. Yes, my father's rich again and very well esteemed in Venice.

BASSANIO. Times are not what they were when gentlemen give place to Jews. Well, God bless you!

PORTIA. You'll drink some wine with us before you go. Bassanio, lead Lorenzo and Jessica to the house. Shylock and I will follow.

BASSANIO. Come, Lorenzo! Jessica! I am almost afraid to walk with you!

JESSICA (*taking his arm*). You need not be, my lord.

[*Exeunt* JESSICA, BASSANIO, *and* LORENZO.

SHYLOCK (*to* PORTIA). Is your cousin, Dr. Bellario, in the house?

PORTIA. I think he is. Do you wish to speak to him?

SHYLOCK. He and I have business together!

PORTIA. Why are you taking Jessica and Lorenzo away?

SHYLOCK. Is it not better that I should?

PORTIA. Perhaps. But if it is not Jessica, it will be someone else. Why do you do this for me?

SHYLOCK.   It is not all for you.   Some part of it's for me.

PORTIA.   For you ?   Do you, then, love Lorenzo that you must have him near you in Venice ?

SHYLOCK.   Love Lorenzo ?   No.   But he has children, Portia, and my blood flows in their veins.   I am a Jew, and every Jew has a passion for posterity.   How else could we have survived ?   We must perpetuate.   When I die, all my goods and property will come to Jessica's sons, and I would like them to grow up in some affection for me. That's why I am taking them back to Venice.   Lorenzo is nothing to me—a foolish, babbling fellow—and I have few illusions left about my daughter.   But they have three sons that may be better than their parents, and when I lose hope in one place, madam, I try to find it in another.

PORTIA.   This business with my cousin, is it about money ?

SHYLOCK.   It is.

PORTIA.   You are lending money to me ?

SHYLOCK.   Yes.

PORTIA.   Why ?

SHYLOCK.   I hardly know, except that I wish you well and that you are a kind woman.

PORTIA.   But many women are kind !

SHYLOCK.   Not to me.   (*They are silent for a moment.*) Shall we go in ?

[PORTIA *begins to laugh.*

SHYLOCK.   Why do you laugh, my lady ?

PORTIA.   Because suddenly I thought to myself, " Shylock's got his pound of flesh ! "

SHYLOCK.   Got it !

PORTIA.   You see us all here as we are : Nerissa with her drunken, faithless husband, Lorenzo deceived by Jessica, and I married to a husband I despise ! . . . Oh, sir, you've won your pound of flesh !   We must seem very despicable in your eyes.

SHYLOCK.   Not you !   O, madam, not you !   I am old and near my death and I have had great trouble, but I have learned much.   Of what use is my pound of flesh to me ?

PORTIA.   Will it not feed your revenge ?

SHYLOCK.   Revenge !   When I sought Antonio's life

I was a bitter-minded man, and cherished hatred in my heart. Sometimes, still, I am full of anger when I hear my race derided. What have we Jews done that we should be loathed and mocked by all mankind ?

PORTIA. You would not acknowledge God, but crucified Him.

SHYLOCK. And have not all men crucified Him ? Yet all men are not damned as Jews are damned ! When I was left in Venice, after Jessica had fled and all my goods and lands were taken from me, I sat in my hungry house and thought of this many times, but never found an answer to my questions, till I learned that we're despised by you because you are despised by us. We are a proud and narrow race, and our pride and narrow minds have ruined us. I have the power to govern men. Here in my breast I feel the power to govern men. My heart stirs when I think of generous government and of kindly races striving each with each for greater love and beauty and finer men and women. But I'm condemned, because I am a Jew, to be a usurer and spend my mind on little furtive schemes for making money.

PORTIA. You have no roots. Your race is shallow in its growth.

SHYLOCK. Yet we are old.

PORTIA. All mankind is old. It's only governments are new. You were a nomad race in Israel, shifting like your own sand ; and you're still a nomad race, rootless, unstable, blown by self-interest round the world, with no place that's your own. There is no hope for Jews, Shylock, till they have learned to share the lot of all of us, to live and, if there be the need, to die for some poor soil they call their native land.

SHYLOCK. We cannot go back, madam—we must go on and mingle with the world and lose ourselves in other men. I know that outward things pass and have no duration. There is nothing left but the goodness which a man performs. And so, I take my son and my daughter and their children back to Venice, because their going may take some harm away from you.

[STEPHANO *is heard, at a distance, singing the song :*
" *Come, master youth, count up your charity.*"]

PORTIA.   And you forgive all that we have done to you ?

SHYLOCK.   I must forgive.   We must all forgive, because we have so much to be forgiven.

PORTIA.   Let us go in !

[SHYLOCK *offers her his arm, and she takes it. They listen for a moment to* STEPHANO'S *song, which grows louder as he approaches. Then they go in together ;* STEPHANO, *still unseen, sings his song to the end. The play is finished.*]

THE FOLGER LIBRARY SHAKESPEARE

Designed to make Shakespeare's classic plays available to the general reader, each edition contains a reliable text with modernized spelling and punctuation, scene-by-scene plot summaries, and explanatory notes clarifying obscure and obsolete expressions. An interpretive essay and accounts of Shakespeare's life and theater form an instructive preface to each play.

Louis B. Wright, General Editor, was the Director of the Folger Shakespeare Library from 1948 until his retirement in 1968. He is the author of *Middle-Class Culture in Elizabethan England, Religion and Empire, Shakespeare for Everyman,* and many other books and essays on the history and literature of the Tudor and Stuart periods.

Virginia Lamar, Assistant Editor, served as research assistant to the Director and Executive Secretary of the Folger Shakespeare Library from 1946 until her death in 1968. She is the author of *English Dress in the Age of Shakespeare* and *Travel and Roads in England,* and coeditor of William Strachey's *Historie of Travell into Virginia Britania.*

The Folger Shakespeare Library

The Folger Library General Reader's Shakespeare

THE FAMOUS HISTORY
OF THE LIFE OF
KING HENRY
THE EIGHTH

by
WILLIAM
SHAKESPEARE

PUBLISHED BY POCKET BOOKS NEW YORK

POCKET BOOKS, a Simon & Schuster division of
GULF & WESTERN CORPORATION
1230 Avenue of the Americas, New York, N.Y. 10020

ISBN: 0-671-82660-3   MC81-1646

First Pocket Books printing May, 1968

10   9   8   7   6   5

Preface

This edition of *Henry VIII* is designed to make available a readable text of Shakespeare's last history play. Written in collaboration with another playwright, *Henry VIII* has been one of Shakespeare's most popular plays in the theatre; its pageantry and its color have made it a favorite stage production in every age since its first performance. In the centuries since Shakespeare, many changes have occurred in the meanings of words, and some clarification of Shakespeare's vocabulary may be helpful. To provide the reader with necessary notes in the most accessible format, we have placed them on the pages facing the text that they explain. We have tried to make these notes as brief and simple as possible. Preliminary to the text we have also included a brief statement of essential information about Shakespeare and his stage. Readers desiring more detailed information should refer to the books suggested in the references, and if still further information is needed, the bibliographies in those books will provide the necessary clues to the literature of the subject.

The early texts of Shakespeare's plays provide only scattered stage directions and no indications of setting, and it is conventional for modern editors to add these to clarify the action. Such additions, and additions to entrances and exits, as well as many indications of act and scene divisions, are placed in square brackets.

All illustrations are from material in the Folger Library collections.

L. B. W.
V. A. L.

September 1, 1967

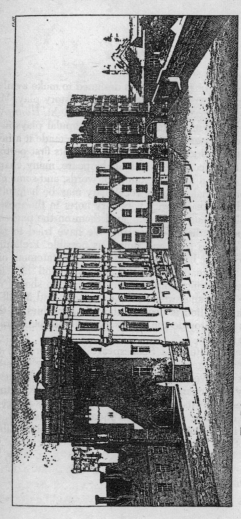

The Palace of Whitehall. Nineteenth-century engraving after a seventeenth-century drawing by Wenceslaus Hollar in the Pepysian Library, Cambridge.

A Play of Popular Pageantry

The Famous History of the Life of King Henry the Eighth was included by Shakespeare's colleagues, Heminges and Condell, in the First Folio of 1623 as the last of Shakespeare's history plays. Through the centuries it has been consistently successful upon the stage. Indeed, few Elizabethan plays have been so regularly seen in the theatre or have attracted greater interest. The popularity of the play owes much to the pageantry and color in a succession of scenes and to the theatrical effectiveness of some of the speeches, which have long been included in collections of the "flowers of Shakespeare." Ironically, most of these speeches are now regarded by many scholars as the handiwork of John Fletcher, the presumed collaborator with Shakespeare in the writing of the play. But no unanimity of opinion prevails. The authorship of *Henry VIII* poses a problem that defies a definitive answer.

Until the middle of the nineteenth century, Shakespeare's authorship of *Henry VIII* was generally accepted, although both Tennyson and Browning, exercising their sensitivity to the nuances of versification in the play, expressed skepticism about Shakespeare's exclusive hand in its composition. In 1850, James Spedding, in an article in *The Gentlemen's Magazine* entitled "Who Wrote Shakespeare's

Henry VIII?," made an elaborate study of the versification and designated John Fletcher, a younger dramatist who supplied plays to Shakespeare's company, as the author of some of the scenes. Another scholar, Samuel Hickson, came to similar conclusions. Hickson, with Spedding's approval, gave the Prologue to Fletcher, Act I, Scs. i and ii, to Shakespeare; Act I, Scs. iii and iv, to Fletcher; Act II, Scs. i and ii, to Fletcher; Act II, Scs. iii and iv, to Shakespeare; Act III, Sc. i, to Fletcher; Act III, Sc. ii, lines 1-205, to Shakespeare; Act III, Sc. ii, lines 206—end, to Fletcher; Act IV, Scs. i and ii, to Fletcher; Act V, Sc. i, to Shakespeare; and the rest to Fletcher. Not every critic has agreed with this division, but the Spedding-Hickson division gained wide currency in the late nineteenth and early twentieth centuries.

More recently, a few scholars have attempted to show that Shakespeare is the sole author. Professor Peter Alexander has been a protagonist of Shakespeare as the only author, and the same position has been taken by R. A. Foakes, editor of the New Arden edition of *Henry VIII* (1957). So the argument goes on. A few scholars have tried to maintain that Philip Massinger wrote portions of the play, but this theory has gained few adherents. Perhaps Sir Edmund Chambers' comments sum up the opinion that is fairly generally held: "I should agree that *Henry VIII* is not very characteristic Fletcher, and should add that it is not very characteristic Shakespeare either. Shakespeare must have been writing in a tired vein and with some loss of concentration. . . . Some kind of collaboration, even if Shakespeare was at a distance, is more plausible than revision, for which there is no clear evidence." Thus Chambers disposes of the notion that Fletcher took a half-finished play by Shakespeare and revised and completed it. He agrees, however, that both writers had a hand in the finished product; that is the most generally held opinion. Barring the discovery of some hitherto unknown external evidence, the problem of the authorship of *Henry VIII* will continue to be a matter of debate.

Although a few scholars have argued that the play had its origins before the death of Queen Elizabeth, the date accepted by most is 1613. A spectacular event helps to date the play, for its performance resulted in the burning down of the Globe playhouse on June 29, 1613, and it was called a new play by commentators on the fire. Sir Henry Wotton, who wrote to Sir Edmund Bacon on July 2, described the fire graphically. He called the play *All Is True*, probably the subtitle (to distinguish it from a hodge-podge of clownery on the reign of Henry by Samuel Rowley called *When You See Me, You Know Me*). Wotton wrote:

"Now to let matters of state sleep, I will entertain you at the present with what happened this week at the Bankside. The King's Players had a new play, called *All Is True*, representing some principal pieces of the reign of Henry VIII, which was set forth with many extraordinary circumstances of pomp and majesty, even to the matting the stage, the Knights of the Order with their Georges and garters, the Guards with their embroidered coats, and the like: sufficient, in truth, within a while to make greatness very familiar if not ridiculous. Now King Henry, making a masque at the Cardinal Wolsey's house, and certain chambers [small cannon] being shot off at his entry, some of the paper or other stuff wherewith one of them was stopped did light on the thatch, where, being thought at first but an idle smoke, and their eyes more attentive to the show, it kindled inwardly and ran round like a train [of gunpowder], consuming within less than an hour the whole house to the very grounds. This was the fatal period of that virtuous fabric wherein yet nothing did perish but wood and straw and a few forsaken cloaks. Only one man had his breeches set on fire that would perhaps have broiled him if he had not by the benefit of provident wit put it out with bottle ale." (Spelling and punctuation are modernized.)

The period from late 1612 through the early part of 1613 was an extraordinarily busy time for the King's Men, as Shakespeare's company of players was designated, because King James had long before taken them under his patronage. The company was called upon to provide fourteen plays for performance at Court during the festivities in 1613 incidental to the visit of Frederick, Elector of the Palatinate, and his subsequent marriage to Princess Elizabeth. Several of Shakespeare's plays were included, but no mention is made by title of *Henry VIII*. Nevertheless, some scholars have argued that Cranmer's prophecy at the christening of Elizabeth Tudor might have been a subtle tribute to the later

Elizabeth which would have made the play suitable for production during the wedding celebrations.

At any rate, the unusual drain on the resources of the King's Men would explain why Shakespeare, who retained his interest in the company, might have been called from retirement at Stratford to help out in the emergency when another new play was needed by the company, even if *Henry VIII* was not written specifically for Court performance. There is no logical reason why he should not have collaborated with one of the talented young playwrights in the employ of the King's Men, namely, John Fletcher.

The structure of *Henry VIII* harks back to some of the earlier chronicle plays. It is a sequence of historical episodes presented like set pieces without much organic relation one to the other. Dramatic critics have found little good to say about the construction of the play. They point out that the interest of the audience focuses in turn upon Buckingham, Katharine, and Wolsey with such intensity that the introduction of Anne Boleyn and the birth of the young Princess Elizabeth come almost as an afterthought. In other words, the play has no central theme that works up to a dramatic climax. It ends, like some of Shakespeare's later romances, and some of the other tragicomedies, on a note of peace and reconciliation.

Though critics may carp, audiences have enjoyed the play from the date of its first performance to our times. After the rebuilding of the Globe, *Henry VIII* was revived in 1628, this time, we can imagine, with more care for the wadding in the cannon firing the salute. The play was revived a few years after the Restoration. Samuel Pepys, who had heard of it as a famous play, presenting "the story of Henry the Eighth with all his wives," as he noted in his *Diary* on December 10, 1663, got around to seeing it on January 1, 1664. But he was disappointed, probably because the play showed only two wives, and he commented sourly: "Saw the much-cried-up play of *Henry the Eighth* . . . made up of patches, that, besides the shows and processions in it, there is nothing in the world good or well done. Thence mightily dissatisfied." But a few years later, on December 30, 1668, he saw it again and changed his opinion: "After dinner my wife and I to the Duke's playhouse and there did see *King Henry the Eighth* and was mightily pleased, better than I ever expected, with the history and show of it."

John Downes, who wrote *Roscius Anglicanus* (1708), provides a bit of interesting information about this play and the continuity of theatrical traditions, for he reported that Thomas Betterton, who played the part of the King in the Restoration revivals, received advice from William Davenant, who had information about the part from "old Mr. Lowen" (John Lowin, one of Shakespeare's fellow players), who had "his Instructions from Mr. Shakespear himself."

The play continued to be popular through most of the eighteenth century. At Drury Lane in 1727 the elaborate coronation of Anne Boleyn was staged with much splendor as a reflection of the public in-

terest in the recent coronation of George II. There is
no indication that the players consciously burlesqued
George's coronation, which was an affair of vulgar
ostentation with his queen decked from head to heel
in blazing jewelry, much of which she had borrowed. Anne's coronation in *Henry VIII* echoed this
event, which pleased the multitude, and the sump-
tuous spectacle became a part of the play's pageantry for years to come.

Although *Henry VIII* had constantly appeared
through most of the eighteenth century, it had an
even greater popularity in the nineteenth, when the
theatres outdid themselves in dramatic spectaculars
and the mounting of realistic sets. In 1855, at the
Princess Theatre in London, Charles Kean put on a
production that had the longest run of any play up
to that time—nearly a hundred nights. He repeated
his success in 1859. In 1892, Henry Irving tried to
outdo Kean with an elaborate production of *Henry
VIII* at the Lyceum Theatre in London, when he
required 203 persons in the cast.

Twentieth-century productions have been less
elaborate, but the play has held the stage consistently. In addition to appearances in the public theatres, it has been performed on academic stages and
in little theatres. In 1946, Christ Church, Oxford, as
part of the celebration of the 400th anniversary of its
founding by Henry VIII, staged the play in its great
hall, built by Wolsey. Tyrone Guthrie directed notable productions at Stratford-upon-Avon in 1949 and
1950 and at the Old Vic in London in 1953.

Many players have delighted in acting the roles of

Buckingham, Katharine, Wolsey, and the King. Mrs. Siddons, "the divine Sarah," starred as Katharine in John Philip Kemble's production of the play in 1788. Later actresses have vied for the part. Mrs. Siddons and her brother, Kemble, who played the role of Wolsey in later revivals, made *Henry VIII* one of the favorite plays of the late eighteenth and early nineteenth centuries. Mrs. Siddons was last seen in the part of Katharine in 1816 and Kemble as Wolsey in 1817.

Henry Irving was a notable Wolsey in the last decade of the nineteenth century. His son declared that it was his best role. In early-twentieth-century productions, Ellen Terry distinguished herself in the role of Katharine.

Although critics have found fault with the writing, actors and actresses have made some of the famous speeches in this play memorable. To critics, words put into the mouths of Wolsey and Katharine appear too smooth and sentimental. On the stage they are effective, as are the processions and pageantry. The author or authors of this play knew the requirements of the theatre, and the popular reception of the play from that day to ours confutes austere criticism that emanates from the study instead of the playhouse.

The main sources of *Henry VIII* are found in Raphael Holinshed's *Chronicles* (1587), and in John Foxe's *Acts and Monuments* (first published in 1563) for the portion on Cranmer. The play twists the facts of history to suit its purposes. For example, in the play Katharine is made to die before Elizabeth's

The Pope suppressed by Henry VIII. From John Foxe, *Acts and Monuments* (1570).

birth in 1533; Katharine actually lived on until 1536. Cranmer's appearance before the Council took place after Elizabeth's christening, not before it. Buckingham's execution occurred before, not after, the tax of 1525. The time of action in the play covers events from the Field of the Cloth of Gold in 1520 until the christening of Elizabeth in September, 1533.

The present text, like that of all editions, is based on the text in the First Folio edition of 1623. Copy for that edition is believed to have been a transcript made from the author's own version rather than a playhouse prompt copy. Some of the elaborate stage directions as they have come down to us are clearly the author's own. The Folio text is well printed and has relatively few errors. The play in the Folio text is divided into acts and scenes.

THE AUTHOR

As early as 1598 Shakespeare was so well known as a literary and dramatic craftsman that Francis Meres, in his *Palladis Tamia: Wits Treasury,* referred in flattering terms to him as "mellifluous and honey-tongued Shakespeare," famous for his *Venus and Adonis,* his *Lucrece,* and "his sugared sonnets," which were circulating "among his private friends." Meres observes further that "as Plautus and Seneca are accounted the best for comedy and tragedy among the Latins, so Shakespeare among the English is the most excellent in both kinds for the stage," and he mentions a dozen plays that had made a name for Shakespeare. He concludes with the remark that "the Muses would speak with Shakespeare's fine filed phrase if they would speak English."

To those acquainted with the history of the Elizabethan and Jacobean periods, it is incredible that anyone should be so naïve or ignorant as to doubt the reality of Shakespeare as the author of the plays that bear his name. Yet so much nonsense has been written about other "candidates" for the plays that it is well to remind readers that no credible evidence that would stand up in a court of law has ever been adduced to prove either that Shakespeare did not write his plays or that anyone else wrote them. All the theories offered for the authorship of Francis Bacon, the Earl of Derby, the Earl of Oxford, the Earl of Hertford, Christopher Marlowe, and a score of other candidates are mere conjectures spun from the active imaginations of persons who confuse hypothesis and conjecture with evidence.

As Meres's statement of 1598 indicates, Shakespeare was already a popular playwright whose name carried weight at the box office. The obvious reputation of Shakespeare as early as 1598 makes the effort to prove him a myth one of the most absurd in the history of human perversity.

The anti-Shakespeareans talk darkly about a plot of vested interests to maintain the authorship of Shakespeare. Nobody has any vested interest in Shakespeare, but every scholar is interested in the truth and in the quality of evidence advanced by special pleaders who set forth hypotheses in place of facts.

The anti-Shakespeareans base their arguments upon a few simple premises, all of them false. These false premises are that Shakespeare was an unlettered yokel without any schooling, that nothing is known about Shakespeare, and that only a noble lord or the equivalent in background could have written the plays. The facts are that more is known about Shakespeare than about most dramatists of his day, that he had a very good education, acquired in the Stratford Grammar School, that the plays show no evidence of profound book learning, and that the knowledge of kings and courts evident in the plays is no greater than any intelligent young man could have picked up at second hand. Most anti-Shakespeareans are naïve and betray an obvious snobbery. The author of their favorite plays, they imply, must have had a college diploma framed and hung on his study wall like the one in their dentist's office, and obviously so great a writer must have had a title or some equally significant evidence of exalted social background. They forget that genius has a way of cropping up in unexpected places and that none of the great creative writers of the world got his inspiration in a college or university course.

William Shakespeare was the son of John Shakespeare of Stratford-upon-Avon, a substantial citizen of that small but busy market town in the center of the rich agricultural county of Warwick. John Shakespeare kept a shop, what we would call a general store; he dealt in wool and other produce and gradually acquired property. As a youth, John Shakespeare had learned the trade of glover and leather worker. There is no contemporary evidence that the elder Shakespeare was a butcher, though the anti-Shakespeareans like to talk about the ignorant "butcher's boy of Stratford." Their only evidence is a statement by gossipy John Aubrey, more than a century after William Shakespeare's birth, that young William followed his father's trade, and when he killed a calf, "he would do it in a high style and make a speech." We would like to believe the story true, but Aubrey is not a very credible witness.

John Shakespeare probably continued to operate a farm at Snitterfield that his father had leased. He married Mary Arden, daughter of his father's landlord, a man of some property. The third of their eight children was William, baptized on April 26, 1564, and probably born three days before. At least, it is conventional to celebrate April 23 as his birthday.

The Stratford records give considerable information about John Shakespeare. We know that he held several municipal offices including those of alderman and mayor. In 1580 he was in some sort of legal difficulty and was fined for neglecting a summons of the Court of Queen's Bench requiring him to appear at Westminster and be bound over to keep the peace.

As a citizen and alderman of Stratford, John Shakespeare was entitled to send his son to the grammar school free. Though the records are lost, there can be no reason to doubt that this is where young William received his education. As any student of the period knows, the grammar schools provided the basic education in Latin learning and literature. The Elizabethan grammar school is not to be confused with modern grammar schools. Many

cultivated men of the day received all their formal
education in the grammar schools. At the universities in this period a student would have received
little training that would have inspired him to be a
creative writer. At Stratford young Shakespeare
would have acquired a familiarity with Latin and
some little knowledge of Greek. He would have
read Latin authors and become acquainted with
the plays of Plautus and Terence. Undoubtedly, in
this period of his life he received that stimulation
to read and explore for himself the world of ancient
and modern history which he later utilized in his
plays. The youngster who does not acquire this
type of intellectual curiosity *before* college days
rarely develops as a result of a college course the
kind of mind Shakespeare demonstrated. His learning in books was anything but profound, but he
clearly had the probing curiosity that sent him in
search of information, and he had a keenness in the
observation of nature and of humankind that finds
reflection in his poetry.

There is little documentation for Shakespeare's
boyhood. There is little reason why there should
be. Nobody knew that he was going to be a dramatist about whom any scrap of information would be
prized in the centuries to come. He was merely an
active and vigorous youth of Stratford, perhaps as-
sisting his father in his business, and no Boswell
bothered to write down facts about him. The most
important record that we have is a marriage license
issued by the Bishop of Worcester on November
27, 1582, to permit William Shakespeare to marry

Anne Hathaway, seven or eight years his senior; furthermore, the Bishop permitted the marriage after reading the banns only once instead of three times, evidence of the desire for haste. The need was explained on May 26, 1583, when the christening of Susanna, daughter of William and Anne Shakespeare, was recorded at Stratford. Two years later, on February 2, 1585, the records show the birth of twins to the Shakespeares, a boy and a girl who were christened Hamnet and Judith.

What William Shakespeare was doing in Stratford during the early years of his married life, or when he went to London, we do not know. It has been conjectured that he tried his hand at schoolteaching, but that is a mere guess. There is a legend that he left Stratford to escape a charge of poaching in the park of Sir Thomas Lucy of Charlecote, but there is no proof of this. There is also a legend that when first he came to London he earned his living by holding horses outside a playhouse and presently was given employment inside, but there is nothing better than eighteenth-century hearsay for this. How Shakespeare broke into the London theatres as a dramatist and actor we do not know. But lack of information is not surprising, for Elizabethans did not write their autobiographies, and we know even less about the lives of many writers and some men of affairs than we know about Shakespeare. By 1592 he was so well established and popular that he incurred the envy of the dramatist and pamphleteer Robert Greene, who referred to him as an "upstart crow . . . in his own conceit the only Shake-scene in a country." From this time onward, contemporary allusions and references in legal documents enable the scholar to chart Shakespeare's career with greater accuracy than is possible with most other Elizabethan dramatists.

By 1594 Shakespeare was a member of the company of actors known as the Lord Chamberlain's Men. After the accession of James I, in 1603, the company would have the sovereign for their patron and would be known as the King's Men. During the period of its greatest prosperity, this company would have as its principal theatres the Globe and the Blackfriars. Shakespeare was both an actor and a shareholder in the company. Tradition has assigned him such acting roles as Adam in *As You Like It* and the Ghost in *Hamlet,* a modest place on the stage that suggests that he may have had other duties in the management of the company. Such conclusions, however, are based on surmise.

What we do know is that his plays were popular and that he was highly successful in his vocation. His first play may have been *The Comedy of Errors,* acted perhaps in 1591. Certainly this was one of his earliest plays. The three parts of *Henry VI* were acted sometime between 1590 and 1592. Critics are not in agreement about precisely how much Shakespeare wrote of these three plays. *Richard III* probably dates from 1593. With this play Shakespeare captured the imagination of Elizabethan audiences, then enormously interested in historical plays. With *Richard III* Shakespeare also gave an interpretation pleasing to the Tudors of the rise to power of the grandfather of Queen Elizabeth. From this time onward, Shakespeare's plays followed on the stage in rapid succession: *Titus Andronicus, The Taming of the Shrew, The Two Gentlemen of Verona, Love's Labor's Lost, Romeo and Juliet, Richard II, A Midsummer Night's Dream, King John, The Merchant of Venice, Henry IV (Parts 1 and 2), Much Ado about Nothing, Henry V, Julius Caesar, As You Like It, Twelfth Night, Hamlet, The Merry Wives of Windsor, All's Well That Ends Well, Measure for Measure, Othello, King Lear,* and nine others that followed before Shakespeare retired completely, about 1613.

In the course of his career in London, he made enough money to enable him to retire to Stratford with a competence. His purchase on May 4, 1597, of New Place, then the second-largest dwelling in Stratford, "a pretty house of brick and timber," with a handsome garden, indicates his increasing prosperity. There his wife and children lived while he busied himself in the London theatres. The summer before he acquired New Place, his life was darkened by the death of his only son, Hamnet, a child of eleven. In May, 1602, Shakespeare purchased one hundred and seven acres of fertile farmland near Stratford and a few months later bought a cottage and garden across the alley from New Place. About 1611, he seems to have returned permanently to Stratford, for the next year a legal document refers to him as "William Shakespeare of Stratford-upon-Avon . . . gentleman." To achieve the desired appellation of gentleman, William Shakespeare had seen to it that the College of Heralds in 1596 granted his father a coat of arms. In one step he thus became a second-generation gentleman.

Shakespeare's daughter Susanna made a good match in 1607 with Dr. John Hall, a prominent and prosperous Stratford physician. His second daughter, Judith, did not marry until she was thirty-one years old, and then, under somewhat scandalous circumstances, she married Thomas Quiney, a Stratford vintner. On March 25, 1616, Shakespeare made his will, bequeathing his landed property to Susanna, £300 to Judith, certain sums to other relatives, and his second-best bed to his wife, Anne. Much has been made of the second-best bed, but the legacy probably indicates only that Anne liked that particular bed. Shakespeare, following the practice of the time, may have already arranged with Susanna for his wife's care. Finally, on April 23, 1616, the anniversary of his birth, William Shakespeare died, and he was buried on April 25 within the chancel of Trinity Church, as befitted an honored citizen. On August 6, 1623, a few months before the publication of the collected edition of Shakespeare's plays, Anne Shakespeare joined her husband in death.

THE PUBLICATION OF HIS PLAYS

During his lifetime Shakespeare made no effort to publish any of his plays, though eighteen appeared in print in single-play editions known as quartos. Some of these are corrupt versions known as "bad quartos." No quarto, so far as is known, had the author's approval. Plays were not considered "literature" any more than most radio and television scripts today are considered literature. Dramatists sold their plays outright to the theatrical companies and it was usually considered in the company's interest to keep plays from getting into print. To achieve a reputation as a man of letters, Shakespeare wrote his *Sonnets* and his narrative poems, *Venus and Adonis* and *The Rape of Lucrece*, but he probably never dreamed that his plays would establish his reputation as a literary genius. Only Ben Jonson, a man known for his colossal conceit, had the crust to call his plays *Works*, as he did when he published an edition in 1616. But men laughed at Ben Jonson.

After Shakespeare's death, two of his old colleagues in the King's Men, John Heminges and Henry Condell, decided that it would be a good thing to print, in more accurate versions than were then available, the plays already published and eighteen additional plays not previously published in quarto. In 1623 appeared *Mr. William Shakespeares Comedies, Histories & Tragedies. Published according to the True Originall Copies. London. Printed by Isaac Iaggard and Ed. Blount.* This was the famous First Folio, a work that had the authority of Shakespeare's associates. The only play commonly attributed to Shakespeare that was omitted in the First Folio was *Pericles*. In their preface,

"To the great Variety of Readers," Heminges and Condell state that whereas "you were abused with diverse stolen and surreptitious copies, maimed and deformed by the frauds and stealths of injurious impostors that exposed them, even those are now offered to your view cured and perfect of their limbs; and all the rest, absolute in their numbers, as he conceived them." What they used for printer's copy is one of the vexed problems of scholarship, and skilled bibliographers have devoted years of study to the question of the relation of the "copy" for the First Folio to Shakespeare's manuscripts. In some cases it is clear that the editors corrected printed quarto versions of the plays, probably by comparison with playhouse scripts. Whether these scripts were in Shakespeare's autograph is anybody's guess. No manuscript of any play in Shakespeare's handwriting has survived. Indeed, very few play manuscripts from this period by any author are extant. The Tudor and Stuart periods had not yet learned to prize autographs and authors' original manuscripts.

Since the First Folio contains eighteen plays not previously printed, it is the only source for these. For the other eighteen, which had appeared in quarto versions, the First Folio also has the authority of an edition prepared and overseen by Shakespeare's colleagues and professional associates. But since editorial standards in 1623 were far from strict, and Heminges and Condell were actors rather than editors by profession, the texts are sometimes careless. The printing and proofreading of the First

Folio also left much to be desired, and some garbled passages have had to be corrected and emended. The "good quarto" texts have to be taken into account in preparing a modern edition.

Because of the great popularity of Shakespeare through the centuries, the First Folio has become a prized book, but it is not a very rare one, for it is estimated that 238 copies are extant. The Folger Shakespeare Library in Washington, D.C., has seventy-nine copies of the First Folio, collected by the founder, Henry Clay Folger, who believed that a collation of as many texts as possible would reveal significant facts about the text of Shakespeare's plays. Dr. Charlton Hinman, using an ingenious machine of his own invention for mechanical collating, has made many discoveries that throw light on Shakespeare's text and on printing practices of the day.

The probability is that the First Folio of 1623 had an edition of between 1,000 and 1,250 copies. It is believed that it sold for £1, which made it an expensive book, for £1 in 1623 was equivalent to something between $40 and $50 in modern purchasing power.

During the seventeenth century, Shakespeare was sufficiently popular to warrant three later editions in folio size, the Second Folio of 1632, the Third Folio of 1663–1664, and the Fourth Folio of 1685. The Third Folio added six other plays ascribed to Shakespeare, but these are apocryphal.

THE SHAKESPEAREAN THEATRE

The theatres in which Shakespeare's plays were performed were vastly different from those we know today. The stage was a platform that jutted out into the area now occupied by the first rows of seats on the main floor, which is called the "orchestra" in America and the "pit" in England. This platform had no curtain to come down at the ends of acts and scenes. And although simple stage properties were available, the Elizabethan theatre lacked both the machinery and the elaborate movable scenery of the modern theatre. In the rear of the platform stage was a curtained area that could be used as an inner room, a tomb, or any such scene that might be required. A balcony above this inner room, and perhaps balconies on the sides of the stage, could represent the upper deck of a ship, the entry to Juliet's room, or a prison window. A trap door in the stage provided an entrance for ghosts and devils from the nether regions, and a similar trap in the canopied structure over the stage, known as the "heavens," made it possible to let down angels on a rope. These primitive stage arrangements help to account for many elements in Elizabethan plays. For example, since there was no curtain, the dramatist frequently felt the necessity of writing into his play action to clear the stage at the ends of acts and scenes. The funeral march at the end of *Hamlet* is not there merely for atmosphere; Shakespeare had to get the corpses off the stage. The lack of scenery also freed the dramatist from undue concern about the exact location of his sets, and the physical relation of his various settings to each other did not have to be worked out with the same precision as in the modern theatre.

Before London had buildings designed exclusively for theatrical entertainment, plays were given in inns and taverns. The characteristic inn of the period had an inner courtyard with rooms opening onto balconies overlooking the yard. Players could set up their temporary stages at one end of the yard and audiences could find seats on the balconies out of the weather. The poorer sort could stand or sit on the cobblestones in the yard, which was open to the sky. The first theatres followed this construction, and throughout the Elizabethan period the large public theatres had a yard in front of the stage open to the weather, with two or three tiers of covered balconies extending around the theatre. This physical structure again influenced the writing of plays. Because a dramatist wanted the actors to be heard, he frequently wrote into his play orations that could be delivered with declamatory effect. He also provided spectacle, buffoonery, and broad jests to keep the riotous groundlings in the yard entertained and quiet.

In another respect the Elizabethan theatre differed greatly from ours. It had no actresses. All women's roles were taken by boys, sometimes recruited from the boys' choirs of the London churches. Some of these youths acted their roles with great skill and the Elizabethans did not seem to be aware of any incongruity. The first actresses on the professional English stage appeared after the Restoration of Charles II, in 1660, when exiled Englishmen brought back from France practices of the French stage.

London in the Elizabethan period, as now, was the center of theatrical interest, though wandering actors from time to time traveled through the country performing in inns, halls, and the houses of the nobility. The first professional playhouse, called simply The Theatre, was erected by James Burbage, father of Shakespeare's colleague Richard Burbage, in 1576 on lands of the old Holywell Priory adjacent to Finsbury Fields, a playground and park area just north of the city walls. It had the advantage of being outside the city's jurisdiction and yet was near enough to be easily accessible. Soon after The Theatre was opened, another playhouse called The Curtain was erected in the same neighborhood. Both of these playhouses had open courtyards and were probably polygonal in shape.

About the time The Curtain opened, Richard Farrant, Master of the Children of the Chapel Royal at Windsor and of St. Paul's, conceived the idea of opening a "private" theatre in the old monastery buildings of the Blackfriars, not far from St. Paul's Cathedral in the heart of the city. This theatre was ostensibly to train the choirboys in plays for presentation at Court, but Farrant managed to present plays to paying audiences and achieved considerable success until aristocratic neighbors complained and had the theatre closed. This first Blackfriars Theatre was significant, however, because it popularized the boy actors in a professional way and it paved the way for a second theatre in the Blackfriars, which Shakespeare's company took over more than thirty years later. By the last years of the sixteenth century, London had at least six professional theatres and still others were erected during the reign of James I.

The Globe Theatre, the playhouse that most people connect with Shakespeare, was erected early in 1599 on the Bankside, the area across the Thames from the city. Its construction had a dramatic beginning, for on the night of December 28, 1598, James Burbage's sons, Cuthbert and Richard, gathered together a crew who tore down the old theatre in Holywell and carted the timbers across the river to a site that they had chosen for a new playhouse. The reason for this clandestine operation was a row with the landowner over the lease to the Holywell property. The site chosen for the Globe was another playground outside of the city's jurisdiction, a region of somewhat unsavory character. Not far away was the Bear Garden, an amphitheatre devoted to the baiting of bears and bulls. This was also the region occupied by many houses of ill fame licensed by the Bishop of Winchester and the source of substantial revenue to him. But it was easily accessible either from London Bridge or by means of the cheap boats operated by the London watermen, and it had the great advantage of being beyond the authority of the Puritanical aldermen of London, who frowned on plays because they lured apprentices from work, filled their heads with improper ideas, and generally exerted a bad influence. The aldermen also complained that the crowds drawn together in the theatre helped to spread the plague.

The Globe was the handsomest theatre up to its time. It was a large building, apparently octagonal in shape, and open like its predecessors to the sky in the center, but capable of seating a large audience in its covered balconies. To erect and operate the Globe, the Burbages organized a syndicate composed of the leading members of the dramatic company, of which Shakespeare was a member. Since it was open to the weather and depended on natural light, plays had to be given in the afternoon. This caused no hardship in the long afternoons of an English summer, but in the winter the weather was a great handicap and discouraged all except the hardiest. For that reason, in 1608 Shakespeare's company was glad to take over the lease of the second Blackfriars Theatre, a substantial, roomy hall reconstructed within the framework of the old monastery building. This theatre was protected from the weather and its stage was artificially lighted by chandeliers of candles. This became the winter playhouse for Shakespeare's company and at once proved so popular that the congestion of traffic created an embarrassing problem. Stringent regulations had to be made for the movement of coaches in the vicinity. Shakespeare's company continued to use the Globe during the summer months. In 1613 a squib fired from a cannon during a performance of

Henry VIII fell on the thatched roof and the Globe burned to the ground. The next year it was rebuilt.

London had other famous theatres. The Rose, just west of the Globe, was built by Philip Henslowe, a semiliterate denizen of the Bankside, who became one of the most important theatrical owners and producers of the Tudor and Stuart periods. What is more important for historians, he kept a detailed account book, which provides much of our information about theatrical history in his time. Another famous theatre on the Bankside was the Swan, which a Dutch priest, Johannes de Witt, visited in 1596. The crude drawing of the stage which he made was copied by his friend Arend van Buchell; it is one of the important pieces of contemporary evidence for theatrical construction. Among the other theatres, the Fortune, north of the city, on Golding Lane, and the Red Bull, even farther away from the city, off St. John's Street, were the most popular. The Red Bull, much frequented by apprentices, favored sensational and sometimes rowdy plays.

The actors who kept all of these theatres going were organized into companies under the protection of some noble patron. Traditionally actors had enjoyed a low reputation. In some of the ordinances they were classed as vagrants; in the phraseology of the time, "rogues, vagabonds, sturdy beggars, and common players" were all listed together as undesirables. To escape penalties often meted out to these characters, organized groups of actors managed to gain the protection of various personages of high degree. In the later years of Elizabeth's reign, a group flourished under the name of the Queen's Men; another group had the protection of the Lord Admiral and were known as the Lord Admiral's Men. Edward Alleyn, son-in-law of Philip Henslowe, was the leading spirit in the Lord Admiral's Men. Besides the adult companies, troupes of boy actors from time to time also enjoyed considerable popularity. Among these were the Children of Paul's and the Children of the Chapel Royal.

The company with which Shakespeare had a long association had for its first patron Henry Carey, Lord Hunsdon, the Lord Chamberlain, and hence they were known as the Lord Chamberlain's Men. After the accession of James I, they became the King's Men. This company was the great rival of the Lord Admiral's Men, managed by Henslowe and Alleyn.

All was not easy for the players in Shakespeare's time, for the aldermen of London were always eager for an excuse to close up the Blackfriars and any other theatres in their jurisdiction. The theatres outside the jurisdiction of London were not immune from interference, for they might be shut up by order of the Privy Council for meddling in politics or for various other offenses, or they might be closed in time of plague lest they spread infection. During plague times, the actors usually went on tour and played the provinces wherever they could find an audience. Particularly frightening were the plagues of 1592–1594 and 1613 when the theatres closed and the players, like many other Londoners, had to take to the country.

Though players had a low social status, they enjoyed great popularity, and one of the favorite forms of entertainment at Court was the performance of plays. To be commanded to perform at Court conferred great prestige upon a company of players, and printers frequently noted that fact when they published plays. Several of Shakespeare's plays were performed before the sovereign, and Shakespeare himself undoubtedly acted in some of these plays.

REFERENCES FOR FURTHER READING

Many readers will want suggestions for further reading about Shakespeare and his times. A few references will serve as guides to further study in the enormous literature on the subject. A simple and useful little book is Gerald Sanders, *A Shakespeare Primer* (New York, 1950). *A Companion to Shakespeare Studies*, edited by Harley Granville-Barker and G. B. Harrison (Cambridge, 1934), is a valuable guide. The most recent concise handbook of facts about Shakespeare is Gerald E. Bentley, *Shakespeare: A Biographical Handbook* (New Haven, 1961). More detailed but not so voluminous as to be confusing is Hazelton Spencer, *The Art and Life of William Shakespeare* (New York, 1940), which, like Sanders' and Bentley's handbooks, contains a brief annotated list of useful books on various aspects of the subject. The most detailed and scholarly work providing complete factual information about Shakespeare is Sir Edmund Chambers, *William Shakespeare: A Study of Facts and Problems* (2 vols., Oxford, 1930). A vast amount of general information about a wide variety of Shakespearean material is to be found in *The Reader's Encyclopedia of Shakespeare*, edited by O. J. Campbell and Edward G. Quinn (New York, 1966).

Among other biographies of Shakespeare, Joseph Quincy Adams, *A Life of William Shakespeare* (Boston, 1923) is still an excellent assessment of the essential facts and the traditional information, and Marchette Chute, *Shakespeare of London* (New York, 1949; paperback, 1957) stresses Shakespeare's life in the theatre. Two new biographies of Shakespeare have recently appeared. A. L. Rowse, *William Shakespeare: A Biography* (London, 1963; New York, 1964) provides an appraisal by a distinguished English historian, who dismisses the notion that somebody else wrote Shakespeare's plays as arrant nonsense that runs counter to known historical fact. Peter Quennell, *Shakespeare: A Biography* (Cleveland and New York, 1963) is a sensitive and intelligent survey of what is known and surmised of Shakespeare's life. Louis B. Wright, *Shakespeare for Everyman* (paperback; New York, 1964) discusses the basis of Shakespeare's enduring popularity.

The *Shakespeare Quarterly*, published by the Shakespeare Association of America under the editorship of James G. McManaway, is recommended for those who wish to keep up with current Shakespearean scholarship and stage productions. The

Quarterly includes an annual bibliography of Shakespeare editions and works on Shakespeare published during the previous year.

The question of the authenticity of Shakespeare's plays arouses perennial attention. The theory of hidden cryptograms in the plays is demolished by William F. and Elizebeth S. Friedman, *The Shakespearean Ciphers Examined* (New York, 1957). A succinct account of the various absurdities advanced to suggest the authorship of a multitude of candidates other than Shakespeare will be found in R. C. Churchill, *Shakespeare and His Betters* (Bloomington, Ind., 1959). Another recent discussion of the subject, *The Authorship of Shakespeare*, by James G. McManaway (Washington, D.C., 1962), presents the evidence from contemporary records to prove the identity of Shakespeare the actor-playwright with Shakespeare of Stratford.

Scholars are not in agreement about the details of playhouse construction in the Elizabethan period. John C. Adams presents a plausible reconstruction of the Globe in *The Globe Playhouse: Its Design and Equipment* (Cambridge, Mass., 1942; 2nd rev. ed., 1961). A description with excellent drawings based on Dr. Adams' model is Irwin Smith, *Shakespeare's Globe Playhouse: A Modern Reconstruction in Text and Scale Drawings* (New York, 1956). Other sensible discussions are C. Walter Hodges, *The Globe Restored* (London, 1953) and A. M. Nagler, *Shakespeare's Stage* (New Haven, 1958). Bernard Beckerman, *Shakespeare at the Globe, 1599–1609* (New Haven, 1962; paperback, 1962) discusses Elizabethan staging and acting techniques.

A sound and readable history of the early theatres is Joseph Quincy Adams, *Shakespearean Playhouses: A History of English Theatres from the Beginnings to the Restoration* (Boston, 1917). For detailed, factual information about the Elizabethan and seventeenth-century stages, the definitive reference works are Sir Edmund Chambers, *The Elizabethan Stage* (4 vols., Oxford, 1923) and Gerald E. Bentley, *The Jacobean and Caroline Stages* (5 vols., Oxford, 1941–1956).

Further information on the history of the theatre and related topics will be found in the following titles: T. W. Baldwin, *The Organization and Personnel of the Shakespearean Company* (Princeton, 1927); Lily Bess Campbell, *Scenes and Machines on the English Stage during the Renaissance* (Cambridge, 1923); Esther Cloudman Dunn, *Shakespeare in America* (New York, 1939); George C. D. Odell, *Shakespeare from Betterton to Irving* (2 vols., London, 1931); Arthur Colby Sprague, *Shakespeare and the Actors: The Stage Business in His Plays (1660–1905)* (Cambridge, Mass., 1944) and *Shakespearian Players and Performances* (Cambridge, Mass., 1953); Leslie Hotson, *The Commonwealth and Restoration Stage* (Cambridge, Mass., 1928); Alwin Thaler, *Shakspere to Sheridan: A Book about the Theatre of Yesterday and To-day* (Cambridge, Mass., 1922); George C. Branam, *Eighteenth-Century Adaptations of Shakespeare's Tragedies* (Berkeley, 1956); C. Beecher Hogan, *Shakespeare in the Theatre, 1701–1800* (Oxford, 1957);

Ernest Bradlee Watson, *Sheridan to Robertson: A Study of the 19th-Century London Stage* (Cambridge, Mass., 1926); and Enid Welsford, *The Court Masque* (Cambridge, Mass., 1927).

A brief account of the growth of Shakespeare's reputation is F. E. Halliday, *The Cult of Shakespeare* (London, 1947). A more detailed discussion is given in Augustus Ralli, *A History of Shakespearian Criticism* (2 vols., Oxford, 1932; New York, 1958). Harley Granville-Barker, *Prefaces to Shakespeare* (5 vols., London, 1927–1948; 2 vols., London, 1958) provides stimulating critical discussion of the plays. An older classic of criticism is Andrew C. Bradley, *Shakespearean Tragedy: Lectures on Hamlet, Othello, King Lear, Macbeth* (London, 1904; paperback, 1955). Sir Edmund Chambers, *Shakespeare: A Survey* (London, 1935; paperback, 1958) contains short, sensible essays on thirty-four of the plays, originally written as introductions to single-play editions. Alfred Harbage, *William Shakespeare: A Reader's Guide* (New York, 1963) is a handbook to the reading and appreciation of the plays, with scene synopses and interpretation.

For the history plays see Lily Bess Campbell, *Shakespeare's "Histories": Mirrors of Elizabethan Policy* (Cambridge, 1947); John Palmer, *Political Characters of Shakespeare* (London, 1945; 1961); E. M. W. Tillyard, *Shakespeare's History Plays* (London, 1948); Irving Ribner, *The English History Play in the Age of Shakespeare* (Princeton, 1947; rev. ed., New York, 1965); Max M. Reese, *The Cease of Majesty* (London, 1961); and Arthur

Colby Sprague, *Shakespeare's Histories: Plays for the Stage* (London, 1964). Harold Jenkins, "Shakespeare's History Plays: 1900–1951," *Shakespeare Survey 6* (Cambridge, 1953), 1-15, provides an excellent survey of recent critical opinion on the subject.

A good summary of the problem of the authorship of *Henry VIII* will be found in the New Arden *Henry VIII* (London, 1957), edited by R. A. Foakes. An excellent and brief stage history of the play is given in an introductory chapter by C. B. Young in the New Cambridge edition, *King Henry the Eighth* (Cambridge, 1962). A. C. Partridge, *The Problem of "Henry VIII" Reopened* (Cambridge, 1949) asks if it is "unreasonable to conclude that *Henry VIII* was an unfinished play, left at Shakespeare's retirement in the hands of the Company, and completed, perhaps with his acquiescence, by Fletcher, his successor as principal dramatist of the King's Players."

The comedies are illuminated by the following studies: C. L. Barber, *Shakespeare's Festive Comedy* (Princeton, 1959); John Russell Brown, *Shakespeare and His Comedies* (London, 1957); H. B. Charlton, *Shakespearian Comedy* (London, 1938; 4th ed., 1949); W. W. Lawrence, *Shakespeare's Problem Comedies* (New York, 1931); and Thomas M. Parrott, *Shakespearean Comedy* (New York, 1949).

Further discussions of Shakespeare's tragedies, in addition to Bradley, already cited, are contained in H. B. Charlton, *Shakespearian Tragedy* (Cambridge, 1948); Willard Farnham, *The Medieval*

Heritage of Elizabethan Tragedy (Berkeley, 1936) and *Shakespeare's Tragic Frontier: The World of His Final Tragedies* (Berkeley, 1950); and Harold S. Wilson, *On the Design of Shakespearian Tragedy* (Toronto, 1957).

The "Roman" plays are treated in M. M. MacCallum, *Shakespeare's Roman Plays and Their Background* (London, 1910) and J. C. Maxwell, "Shakespeare's Roman Plays, 1900–1956," *Shakespeare Survey 10* (Cambridge, 1957), 1-11.

Kenneth Muir, *Shakespeare's Sources: Comedies and Tragedies* (London, 1957) discusses Shakespeare's use of source material. The sources themselves have been reprinted several times. Among old editions are John P. Collier (ed.), *Shakespeare's Library* (2 vols., London, 1850), Israel C. Gollancz (ed.), *The Shakespeare Classics* (12 vols., London, 1907–1926), and W. C. Hazlitt (ed.), *Shakespeare's Library* (6 vols., London, 1875). A modern edition is being prepared by Geoffrey Bullough with the title *Narrative and Dramatic Sources of Shakespeare* (London and New York, 1957–). Six volumes, covering all the plays except the tragedies, have been published to date (1967).

In addition to the second edition of *Webster's New International Dictionary*, which contains most of the unusual words used by Shakespeare, the following reference works are helpful: Edwin A. Abbott, *A Shakespearian Grammar* (London, 1872); C. T. Onions, *A Shakespeare Glossary* (2nd rev. ed., Oxford, 1925); and Eric Partridge, *Shakespeare's Bawdy* (New York, 1948; paperback, 1960).

Some knowledge of the social background of the period in which Shakespeare lived is important for a full understanding of his work. A brief, clear, and accurate account of Tudor history is S. T. Bindoff, *The Tudors,* in the Penguin series. A readable general history is G. M. Trevelyan, *The History of England,* first published in 1926 and available in numerous editions. The same author's *English Social History,* first published in 1942 and also available in many editions, provides fascinating information about England in all periods. Sir John Neale, *Queen Elizabeth* (London, 1935; paperback, 1957), is the best study of the great Queen. Various aspects of life in the Elizabethan period are treated in Louis B. Wright, *Middle-Class Culture in Elizabethan England* (Chapel Hill, N.C., 1935; reprinted Ithaca, N.Y., 1958, 1964). *Shakespeare's England: An Account of the Life and Manners of His Age,* edited by Sidney Lee and C. T. Onions (2 vols., Oxford, 1917), provides much information on many aspects of Elizabethan life. A fascinating survey of the period will be found in Muriel St. C. Byrne, *Elizabethan Life in Town and Country* (London, 1925; rev. ed., 1954; paperback, 1961).

The Folger Library is issuing a series of illustrated booklets entitled "Folger Booklets on Tudor and Stuart Civilization," printed and distributed by Cornell University Press. Published to date are the following titles:

D. W. Davies, *Dutch Influences on English Culture, 1558–1625*

Giles E. Dawson, *The Life of William Shakespeare*

Ellen C. Eyler, *Early English Gardens and Garden Books*

Elaine W. Fowler, *English Sea Power in the Early Tudor Period, 1485–1558*

John R. Hale, *The Art of War and Renaissance England*

William Haller, *Elizabeth I and the Puritans*

Virginia A. LaMar, *English Dress in the Age of Shakespeare*

———, *Travel and Roads in England*

John L. Lievsay, *The Elizabethan Image of Italy*

James G. McManaway, *The Authorship of Shakespeare*

Dorothy E. Mason, *Music in Elizabethan England*

Garrett Mattingly, *The "Invincible" Armada and Elizabethan England*

Boies Penrose, *Tudor and Early Stuart Voyaging*

Conyers Read, *The Government of England under Elizabeth*

T. I. Rae, *Scotland in the Time of Shakespeare*

Albert J. Schmidt, *The Yeoman in Tudor and Stuart England*

Lilly C. Stone, *English Sports and Recreations*

Craig R. Thompson, *The Bible in English, 1525–1611*

———, *The English Church in the Sixteenth Century*

———, *Schools in Tudor England*

———, *Universities in Tudor England*

Louis B. Wright, *Shakespeare's Theatre and the Dramatic Tradition*

At intervals the Folger Library plans to gather these booklets in hardbound volumes. The first is *Life and Letters in Tudor and Stuart England, First Folger Series,* edited by Louis B. Wright and Virginia A. LaMar (published for the Folger Shakespeare Library by Cornell University Press, 1962). The volume contains eleven of the separate booklets.

[Dramatis Personae

King Henry the Eighth.
Cardinal Wolsey.
Cardinal Campeius.
Capucius, Ambassador from the Emperor Charles V.
Cranmer, Archbishop of Canterbury.
Thomas Howard, Duke of Norfolk.
Edward Stafford, Duke of Buckingham.
Charles Brandon, Duke of Suffolk.
Thomas Howard, Earl of Surrey.
Lord Chamberlain.
Lord Chancellor.
Stephen Gardiner, the King's Secretary and afterward
    Bishop of Winchester.
John Longland, Bishop of Lincoln.
George Neville, 3d Baron Abergavenny.
Sir William Sands, Baron Sands of the Vine.
Sir Henry Guildford.
Sir Thomas Lovell.
Sir Anthony Denny.
Sir Nicholas Vaux.
Secretaries to Wolsey.
Thomas Cromwell, servant to Wolsey.
Griffith, gentleman-usher to Queen Katharine.
Three Gentlemen.
Dr. [Sir William] Butts, physician to King Henry.
Garter King of Arms.
Surveyor to the Duke of Buckingham.
Brandon.
Sergeant at Arms.
Lord Mayor and Aldermen of London.
Doorkeeper of the Council chamber.

Porter and his Man.   Page to Gardiner.   A Crier.

Queen Katharine, wife to *King Henry,* afterward Princess
   Dowager.
Anne Bullen, maid of honor to *Queen Katharine,* after-
   ward Queen.
An Old Lady, friend to *Anne Bullen.*
Patience, woman to *Queen Katharine.*

Bishops, Lords, and Ladies in the dumb shows; Women
attending Queen Katharine; Scribes, Officers, Guards,
and other Attendants; Spirits in Queen Katharine's vision.

SCENE: *London, Westminster, Kimbolton.*]

THE FAMOUS HISTORY
OF THE LIFE OF
KING HENRY
THE EIGHTH

ACT I

Pro. The Prologue warns that the audience is about to see a serious drama, based on truth and presented with gravity.

⁂

3. Sad: solemn; **high:** lofty; **working:** affecting the emotions.

12. undertake: guarantee; **shilling:** the admission fee for one of the more expensive seats in the playhouse.

15. noise of targets: i.e., din made by weapons against shields **(targets).**

16. motley: multicolored; **guarded:** trimmed. The allusion is probably to the appearance of Will Sommers, Henry VIII's personal jester, as a character in Samuel Rowley's *When You See Me, You Know Me* (1605), which also treated the life of the King and contained a fight with swords and targets.

17. deceived: cheated; **gentle:** courteous.

19-20. forfeiting/ Our own brains: losing our credit for intelligence.

20. the opinion that we bring: i.e., the claim we present.

21. make that only true we now intend: i.e., give a wholly truthful presentation.

22. understanding: sympathetic, with a pun referring to the groundlings, "standing" in the yard of the playhouse.

THE PROLOGUE

I come no more to make you laugh: things now
That bear a weighty and a serious brow,
Sad, high, and working, full of state and woe,
Such noble scenes as draw the eye to flow,
We now present. Those that can pity here   5
May, if they think it well, let fall a tear:
The subject will deserve it. Such as give
Their money out of hope they may believe
May here find truth too. Those that come to see
Only a show or two and so agree   10
The play may pass, if they be still and willing,
I'll undertake may see away their shilling
Richly in two short hours. Only they
That come to hear a merry bawdy play,
A noise of targets, or to see a fellow   15
In a long motley coat guarded with yellow,
Will be deceived; for, gentle hearers, know,
To rank our chosen truth with such a show
As fool and fight is, beside forfeiting
Our own brains and the opinion that we bring   20
To make that only true we now intend,
Will leave us never an understanding friend.

24. **happiest:** most intelligent.
27. **As:** as if.

WILL. SOMMERS,
KING HENRY THE EIGHT'S JESTER..

Tho.ˢ Hurst. Edwᵈ Chance & Cᵒ London.

Therefore, for goodness' sake, and as you are known
The first and happiest hearers of the town,
Be sad, as we would make ye. Think ye see   25
The very persons of our noble story
As they were living. Think you see them great
And followed with the general throng and sweat
Of thousand friends. Then, in a moment, see
How soon this mightiness meets misery: 30
And if you can be merry then, I'll say
A man may weep upon his wedding day.

I.i. The Duke of Norfolk describes to the Dukes of Buckingham and Abergavenny the splendors of King Henry's meeting with Francis, King of France, at the Field of the Cloth of Gold. The pomp was arranged by the all-powerful Cardinal Wolsey, whose arrogance has made him unpopular with the nobility. The treaty arranged in France has already been broken by the French, and all agree that the expedition has cost far more than it was worth. Norfolk warns Buckingham that the hostility between the Cardinal and himself is well known; he had best beware Wolsey's power. They observe Wolsey passing by but do not hear him speak of Buckingham and a report from his surveyor, by which Wolsey expects to humble the Duke. Buckingham declares that he will tell the King of Wolsey's schemes with France and the Emperor. Before he can make such a move, Wolsey informs the King of the surveyor's charges, which lead to Buckingham's arrest for high treason.

‖‖‖‖‖‖‖‖‖‖‖‖‖‖‖‖‖‖‖‖‖‖‖‖‖‖

5. **fresh:** unflagging.

9. **suns of glory:** Henry VIII and Francis I, King of France, when they met on the Field of the Cloth of Gold, between Guînes and Ardres, in June, 1520.

14. **as:** as if.

16. **weighed:** balanced.

ACT I

Scene I. [London. An antechamber in the Palace.]

*Enter the Duke of Norfolk at one door; at the other,
the Duke of Buckingham and the Lord Abergavenny.*

Buck. Good morrow, and well met. How have ye
 done
Since last we saw in France?
 Nor.   I thank your Grace,
Healthful, and ever since a fresh admirer   5
Of what I saw there.
 Buck.   An untimely ague
Stayed me a prisoner in my chamber, when
Those suns of glory, those two lights of men,
Met in the vale of Andren.   10
 Nor.   'Twixt Guynes and Arde:
I was then present, saw them salute on horseback;
Beheld them, when they 'lighted, how they clung
In their embracement, as they grew together;
Which had they, what four throned ones could have   15
 weighed
Such a compounded one?

3

23-5. Each following day/ Became the next day's master, till the last/ Made former wonders its: each day surpassed the day before, until the last day repeated all the wonders that had gone before.

26. clinquant: shining.

28. India: proverbially a source of great wealth, hence the eagerness of explorers to find a passage to the Indies.

29. Showed: appeared.

32. pride: magnificent clothing; **that:** so that.

33. as a painting: as good as rouging their cheeks.

34. cried: acclaimed as.

35. Made it a fool and beggar: made it appear by comparison silly and shoddy.

37. As presence did present them: according to which of them was personally present at the moment.

38. Still: always.

40. in censure: i.e., to judge between them.

41. phrase: term.

43. thought's compass: i.e., anyone's imagination.

45. Bevis: Bevis of Hampton, hero of a chivalric romance.

47. belong to worship: am of worshipful (honored) condition, as a member of the nobility.

47-8. affect/ In honor honesty: incline to truthfulness, as befits my honor.

Buck. All the whole time
I was my chamber's prisoner.
   Nor.   Then you lost   20
The view of earthly glory. Men might say,
Till this time pomp was single but now married
To one above itself. Each following day
Became the next day's master, till the last
Made former wonders its. Today the French,   25
All clinquant, all in gold, like heathen gods,
Shone down the English; and tomorrow they
Made Britain India: every man that stood
Showed like a mine. Their dwarfish pages were
As cherubins, all gilt. The madams too,   30
Not used to toil, did almost sweat to bear
The pride upon them, that their very labor
Was to them as a painting. Now this masque
Was cried incomparable; and the ensuing night
Made it a fool and beggar. The two kings,   35
Equal in luster, were now best, now worst,
As presence did present them; him in eye
Still him in praise; and, being present both,
'Twas said they saw but one and no discerner
Durst wag his tongue in censure. When these suns—   40
For so they phrase 'em—by their heralds challenged
The noble spirits to arms, they did perform
Beyond thought's compass, that former fabulous story,
Being now seen possible enough, got credit,
That Bevis was believed.   45
   Buck.   Oh, you go far.
   Nor. As I belong to worship and affect

48. **tract:** course.

51. **To the disposing of it nought rebelled:** no one failed to play his part in the action faithfully.

52. **Order gave each thing view:** each thing was presented in orderly fashion.

52-3. **the office did/ Distinctly his full function:** each official performed his duty perfectly.

58. **certes:** certainly; **no element:** i.e., to have no part in.

61. **ordered:** arranged.

65. **fierce vanities:** immoderate follies.

66. **keech:** lump of animal fat.

67. **Take up the rays o' the beneficial sun:** i.e., monopolize the King's favor.

70. **puts him to these ends:** inspires these actions.

71. **grace:** favorable condition; good fortune.

72. **Chalks successors their way:** smoothes the way for its posterity.

73. **allied:** related.

74. **eminent assistants:** important officers of the government.

75. **self-drawing:** self-spinning; **gives us note:** signifies to us.

In honor honesty, the tract of ev'rything
Would by a good discourser lose some life
Which action's self was tongue to. All was royal: 50
To the disposing of it nought rebelled;
Order gave each thing view; the office did
Distinctly his full function.

    Buck.   Who did guide,
I mean, who set the body and the limbs 55
Of this great sport together?

    Nor.   As you guess,
One, certes, that promises no element
In such a business.

    Buck.   I pray you, who, my lord? 60
    Nor. All this was ordered by the good discretion
Of the right reverend Cardinal of York.

    Buck. The Devil speed him! No man's pie is freed
From his ambitious finger. What had he
To do in these fierce vanities? I wonder 65
That such a keech can with his very bulk
Take up the rays o' the beneficial sun
And keep it from the earth.

    Nor.   Surely, sir,
There's in him stuff that puts him to these ends; 70
For, being not propped by ancestry, whose grace
Chalks successors their way, nor called upon
For high feats done to the Crown; neither allied
To eminent assistants; but, spiderlike,
Out of his self-drawing web, he gives us note, 75
The force of his own merit makes his way;
A gift that Heaven gives for him, which buys

80. **graver:** worthier.

83. **the Devil is a niggard:** i.e., the Devil is too miserly to part with as much pride as Wolsey possesses.

88. **privity:** confidential knowledge.

89. **file:** list.

91. **as great a charge as little honor:** i.e., the honor conferred was not worth the expense of participation.

93. **out:** ignored; omitted.

94. **Must fetch him in he papers:** secures the appearance of whomever he summons.

100. **broke their backs with laying manors on 'em:** i.e., bankrupted themselves by selling land to furnish themselves properly for the French journey.

102-3. **minister communication of/ A most poor issue:** (1) serve notice of impoverished offspring; (2) make possible talks of slight consequence.

105. **values:** equals in value.

A place next to the King.

   Aber.   I cannot tell
What Heaven hath given him: let some graver eye   80
Pierce into that; but I can see his pride
Peep through each part of him. Whence has he that?
If not from hell, the Devil is a niggard,
Or has given all before, and he begins
A new hell in himself.   85

   Buck.   Why the Devil,
Upon this French going out, took he upon him,
Without the privity o' the King, t' appoint
Who should attend on him? He makes up the file
Of all the gentry; for the most part such   90
To whom as great a charge as little honor
He meant to lay upon: and his own letter,
The honorable Board of Council out,
Must fetch him in he papers.

   Aber.   I do know   95
Kinsmen of mine, three at the least, that have
By this so sickened their estates that never
They shall abound as formerly.

   Buck.   Oh, many
Have broke their backs with laying manors on 'em   100
For this great journey. What did this vanity
But minister communication of
A most poor issue?

   Nor.   Grievingly I think,
The peace between the French and us not values   105
The cost that did conclude it.

   Buck.   Every man,

109. **not consulting:** independently.

111. **Dashing:** splashing.

112. **sudden:** violent.

114. **flawed:** broken; **attached:** seized. This actually occurred in March, 1522.

118. **Marry:** indeed ("by the Virgin Mary").

119. **proper title of a peace:** splendid thing to be called peace.

122. **carried:** managed.

123. **Like it your Grace:** if your Grace will forgive my saying so.

130. **wants:** lacks.

131. **minister:** agent.

134. **It reaches far:** referring to the proverb "Kings [and all men of power] have long arms."

135. **Bosom up my counsel:** take my counsel to heart.

After the hideous storm that followed, was
A thing inspired and not consulting broke
Into a general prophecy: that this tempest,   110
Dashing the garment of this peace, aboded
The sudden breach on't.

   Nor.   Which is budded out;
For France hath flawed the league and hath attached
Our merchants' goods at Bordeaux.   115

   Aber.   Is it therefor
The ambassador is silenced?

   Nor.   Marry, is't.

   Aber. A proper title of a peace, and purchased
At a superfluous rate!   120

   Buck.   Why, all this business
Our reverend Cardinal carried.

   Nor.   Like it your Grace,
The state takes notice of the private difference
Betwixt you and Cardinal. I advise you—   125
And take it from a heart that wishes toward you
Honor and plenteous safety—that you read
The Cardinal's malice and his potency
Together; to consider further that
What his high hatred would effect wants not   130
A minister in his power. You know his nature,
That he's revengeful, and I know his sword
Hath a sharp edge: it's long and't may be said
It reaches far, and where 'twill not extend,
Thither he darts it. Bosom up my counsel;   135
You'll find it wholesome. Lo where comes that rock
That I advise your shunning.

SD 137. **Purse:** i.e., the purse that contained the Great Seal of England, which was entrusted to Wolsey as Chancellor.

140. **so please:** if it please.

145. **lessen this big look:** look less menacing than he now does.

146. **butcher's cur:** Wolsey's father was reported to have been a butcher. There was apparently a proverbial saying to the effect that butcher's dogs were vicious.

148-49. **A beggar's book/ Outworths a noble's blood:** i.e., the literacy of a base man is more respected than noble birth.

151. **temp'rance:** restraint; patience; **appliance:** remedy.

155. **abject:** despised.

156. **bores me with some trick:** plots to undermine me by some device. **Bore** is usually associated with "bourd," meaning "mock" or "cheat," but the sense "pierce" may also be present.

159. **choler:** anger; **question:** argue.

*Enter Cardinal Wolsey, the Purse borne before him,
certain of the Guard, and two Secretaries with
papers. The Cardinal in his passage fixeth his eye on
Buckingham, and Buckingham on him, both full of
disdain.*

Wol. The Duke of Buckingham's surveyor, ha?
Where's his examination?

Sec.   Here, so please you.   140

Wol. Is he in person ready?

Sec.   Ay, please your Grace.

Wol. Well, we shall then know more; and Buckingham

Shall lessen this big look.   145

                     Exeunt Cardinal and his Train.

Buck. This butcher's cur is venom-mouthed, and I
Have not the power to muzzle him: therefore, best
Not wake him in his slumber. A beggar's book
Outworths a noble's blood.

Nor.   What, are you chafed?   150
Ask God for temp'rance; that's the appliance only
Which your disease requires.

Buck.   I read in's looks
Matter against me, and his eye reviled
Me as his abject object. At this instant   155
He bores me with some trick. He's gone to the King:
I'll follow and outstare him.

Nor.   Stay, my lord,
And let your reason with your choler question

163. **Self mettle:** his own spirit.

167. **a mouth of honor:** a nobleman's lips; i.e., speaking as one whose birth should earn him respect.

169. **difference:** class distinction.

170. **advised:** cautious.

175. **mounts:** raises.

183. **top proud:** proud to the height.

184. **from the flow of gall I name not:** whom I do not speak of spitefully.

185. **sincere motions:** genuine reasons; **intelligence:** information.

THOMAS WOLSÆVS CARD.
Fortitinæ Variantis opus GVolsÆVS ad alta
Scandit iter dubium, certâ minitante ruinâ

Thomas, Cardinal Wolsey. From Henry Holland, *Herwologia* [1620].

What 'tis you go about. To climb steep hills   160
Requires slow pace at first. Anger is like
A full hot horse, who being allowed his way,
Self mettle tires him. Not a man in England
Can advise me like you. Be to yourself
As you would to your friend.   165
  Buck.   I'll to the King
And from a mouth of honor quite cry down
This Ipswich fellow's insolence, or proclaim
There's difference in no persons.
  Nor.   Be advised;   170
Heat not a furnace for your foe so hot
That it do singe yourself. We may outrun
By violent swiftness that which we run at,
And lose by overrunning. Know you not,
The fire that mounts the liquor till't run o'er   175
In seeming to augment it wastes it? Be advised:
I say again, there is no English soul
More stronger to direct you than yourself,
If with the sap of reason you would quench,
Or but allay, the fire of passion.   180
  Buck.   Sir,
I am thankful to you; and I'll go along
By your prescription. But this top proud fellow—
Whom from the flow of gall I name not, but
From sincere motions—by intelligence   185
And proofs as clear as founts in July when
We see each grain of gravel, I do know
To be corrupt and treasonous.
  Nor.   Say not treasonous.

190. **vouch:** declaration.

194. **subtle:** crafty.

198. **suggests:** tempts.

201. **wrenching:** both "rinsing" and "distortion" are combined.

203. **give me favor:** indulge me; let me go on.

205. **combination:** alliance.

207. **to as much end:** as profitably.

212. **Charles the Emperor:** Charles V. Katharine of Aragon was the sister of his mother Joanna. He visited England in 1520, but consultation with Wolsey was not the motive of his visit.

214. **color:** pretext.

CARLO V·IMP·

The Emperor Charles V. From Pompilio Totti, *Ritratti et elogii di capitani illustri* (1635).

Buck. To the King I'll say't and make my vouch as 190
    strong
As shore of rock. Attend. This holy fox,
Or wolf, or both—for he is equal rav'nous
As he is subtle and as prone to mischief
As able to perform't; his mind and place   195
Infecting one another, yea, reciprocally—
Only to show his pomp as well in France
As here at home, suggests the King our master
To this last costly treaty, the interview
That swallowed so much treasure and like a glass 200
Did break i' the wrenching.
    Nor.   Faith, and so it did.
    Buck. Pray, give me favor, sir. This cunning Cardi-
    nal
The articles o' the combination drew   205
As himself pleased; and they were ratified
As he cried, "Thus let be," to as much end
As give a crutch to the dead. But our Count-Cardinal
Has done this, and 'tis well; for worthy Wolsey,
Who cannot err, he did it. Now this follows—   210
Which, as I take it, is a kind of puppy
To the old dam, treason—Charles the Emperor,
Under pretense to see the Queen his aunt—
For 'twas indeed his color, but he came
To whisper Wolsey—here makes visitation.   215
His fears were that the interview betwixt
England and France might through their amity
Breed him some prejudice; for from this league

220. **trow:** believe.

224. **thus desired:** i.e., requested the action described in the next two lines.

232. **Something mistaken in't:** i.e., that Buckingham somewhat misjudged Wolsey's action.

235. **in proof:** by evidence.

Tilting match. From Raphael Holinshed, *Chronicles* (1577).

Peeped harms that menaced him. He privily
Deals with our Cardinal; and, as I trow—   220
Which I do well, for I am sure the Emperor
Paid ere he promised; whereby his suit was granted
Ere it was asked—but when the way was made
And paved with gold, the Emperor thus desired,
That he would please to alter the King's course   225
And break the foresaid peace. Let the King know,
As soon he shall by me, that thus the Cardinal
Does buy and sell his honor as he pleases,
And for his own advantage.

   Nor.   I am sorry   230
To hear this of him and could wish he were
Something mistaken in't.

   Buck.   No, not a syllable:
I do pronounce him in that very shape
He shall appear in proof.   235

*Enter Brandon, a Sergeant at Arms before him, and
            two or three of the Guard.*

   Bran. Your office, sergeant: execute it.
   Ser.   Sir,
My lord the Duke of Buckingham, and Earl
Of Hereford, Stafford, and Northampton, I
Arrest thee of high treason, in the name   240
Of our most sovereign King.
   Buck.   Lo you, my lord,
The net has fall'n upon me! I shall perish

244. **Under device and practice:** by means of trickery.

246. **look on:** oversee.

254. **Aberga'ny:** always pronounced as four syllables, with the *v* unsounded.

263. **attach:** arrest.

265. **Gilbert Peck:** Given both as Gilbert Perke and Pecke in Holinshed, but the trial documents name him Robert Gilbert.

Under device and practice.

  Bran.   I am sorry   245
To see you ta'en from liberty, to look on
The business present. 'Tis His Highness' pleasure
You shall to the Tower.

  Buck.   It will help me nothing
To plead mine innocence; for that dye is on me 250
Which makes my whit'st part black. The will of
  Heav'n
Be done in this and all things! I obey.
O my Lord Aberga'ny, fare you well!

  Bran. Nay, he must bear you company. [*To Aber-* 255
  gavenny] The King
Is pleased you shall to the Tower till you know
How he determines further.

  Aber.   As the Duke said,
The will of Heaven be done and the King's pleasure 260
By me obeyed!

  Bran. Here is a warrant from
The King t' attach Lord Montacute and the bodies
Of the Duke's confessor, John de la Car,
One Gilbert Peck, his chancellor—   265

  Buck.   So, so;
These are the limbs o' the plot; no more, I hope.

  Bran. A monk o' the Chartreux.

  Buck.   Oh, Nicholas Hopkins?

  Bran.   He. 270

  Buck. My surveyor is false: the o'ergreat Cardinal
Hath showed him gold; my life is spanned already.
I am the shadow of poor Buckingham,

274. **figure:** physical form; **cloud puts on:** clothes itself in cloud; is disgraced.

275. **dark'ning:** angering; **sun:** the King.

‖‖‖‖‖‖‖‖‖‖‖‖‖‖‖‖‖‖‖‖‖‖‖‖‖‖‖‖‖‖‖‖‖‖‖

I.ii. King Henry thanks Wolsey for revealing Buckingham's conspiracy against his life. Queen Katharine interrupts the proceedings to plead for the removal of a tax that has heavily burdened the common people and accuses Wolsey of responsibility. Norfolk confirms that the people are threatening rebellion because of the tax. Wolsey denies responsibility. King Henry, moved by the Queen's words, orders letters sent to every county pardoning the people for failure to pay. Wolsey privately orders his secretary to see to it that he receives credit for settling the people's grievance. Buckingham's surveyor is then heard. He accuses his master of threatening to seize the crown if the King should die without issue. Buckingham is also accused of listening to prophecies that the King and his heirs are ill-fated and that he should court the people in the certainty of becoming King. Buckingham is reported to have spoken of killing King Henry, as his father would have killed Richard III had opportunity offered. The King announces Buckingham's attachment and orders that he be brought to immediate trial.

‖‖‖‖‖‖‖‖‖‖‖‖‖‖‖‖‖‖‖‖‖‖‖‖‖‖‖‖‖

2. **level:** aim.
3. **full-charged:** fully loaded.
6. **justify:** verify.
SD 8. **state:** chair of state.

13

Whose figure even this instant cloud puts on
By dark'ning my clear sun. My lord, farewell.   275
                   Exeunt.

Scene II. [London. The Council chamber.]

*Cornets. Enter King Henry, leaning on the Cardinal's
shoulder; the Nobles, and Sir Thomas Lovell: the
Cardinal places himself under the King's feet on his
right side.*

King. My life itself, and the best heart of it,
Thanks you for this great care. I stood i' the level
Of a full-charged confederacy and give thanks
To you that choked it. Let be called before us
That gentleman of Buckingham's. In person   5
I'll hear him his confessions justify;
And point by point the treasons of his master
He shall again relate.

*A noise within, crying, "Room for the Queen!" Enter
Queen Katharine, ushered by the Duke of Norfolk,
and the Duke of Suffolk: she kneels. The King riseth
from his state, takes her up, kisses and placeth her by
him.*

Queen. Nay, we must longer kneel: I am a suitor.
King. Arise and take place by us. Half your suit   10
Never name to us: you have half our power.

12. **moiety:** half-portion.

13. **Repeat your will and take it:** compare the proverb "Ask and have."

21. **true condition:** loyal nature.

40. **Daring the event to the teeth:** i.e., rashly risking the consequences.

The other moiety ere you ask is given.
Repeat your will and take it.
   Queen.   Thank your Majesty.
That you would love yourself, and in that love   15
Not unconsidered leave your honor nor
The dignity of your office, is the point
Of my petition.
   King.   Lady mine, proceed.
   Queen. I am solicited, not by a few,   20
And those of true condition, that your subjects
Are in great grievance. There have been commissions
Sent down among 'em which hath flawed the heart
Of all their loyalties: wherein although,
My good lord Cardinal, they vent reproaches   25
Most bitterly on you as putter-on
Of these exactions, yet the King our master—
Whose honor Heaven shield from soil!—even he
    escapes not
Language unmannerly, yea, such which breaks   30
The sides of loyalty and almost appears
In loud rebellion.
   Nor.   Not almost appears:
It doth appear; for, upon these taxations,
The clothiers all, not able to maintain   35
The many of them 'longing, have put off
The spinsters, carders, fullers, weavers, who,
Unfit for other life, compelled by hunger
And lack of other means, in desperate manner,
Daring the event to the teeth, are all in uproar,   40

41. danger serves among them: violence seems to serve their turn.

48-9. front but in that file/ Where others tell steps with me: am only the most conspicuous person in a group of equal power. In other words, he disclaims sole responsibility for the unpopular tax, apparently the "Amicable Grant" of 1525, an exaction of one sixth of the movables and income of laymen.

52. alike: to everyone.

55. Perforce: whether they will or no.

60. exclamation: accusation.

61. Still exaction: that word "exaction" again.

66. grief: grievance.

HENRICVS D G VIII ANGLIÆ, FRAN, ET HIB, REX ⓒ
Fortibus HENRICVS solitus dare iura BRITANNOS
Fulsum vel Martis vertere et Victeliæ munimenti
Unde armis reanum figuris videte refertæ.

Henry VIII. From Henry Holland, *Herwologia* [1620].

15

And danger serves among them.

    King.   Taxation!
Wherein? and what taxaticn? My lord Cardinal,
You that are blamed for it alike with us,
Know you of this taxation?   45

    Wol.   Please you, sir,
I know but of a single part in aught
Pertains to the state and front but in that file
Where others tell steps with me.

    Queen.   No, my lord?   50
You know no more than others? But you frame
Things that are known alike, which are not whole-
    some
To those which would not know them and yet must
Perforce be their acquaintance. These exactions,   55
Whereof my sovereign would have note, they are
Most pestilent to the hearing; and, to bear 'em,
The back is sacrifice to the load. They say
They are devised by you; or else you suffer
Too hard an exclamation.   60

    King.   Still exaction!
The nature of it? In what kind, let's know,
Is this exaction?

    Queen. I am much too venturous
In tempting of your patience but am boldened   65
Under your promised pardon. The subjects' grief
Comes through commissions, which compels from
    each
The sixth part of his substance, to be levied
Without delay; and the pretense for this   70

79. **primer:** more urgent.

82. **for me:** for my part.

84. **single voice:** unanimous approval.

87. **faculties:** operations.

89. **place:** high estate; **brake:** thicket.

92. **cope:** encounter.

94. **new trimmed:** newly prepared to sail.

96. **sick:** ill-disposed; malicious; **once weak ones:** for that matter, ones incapable of understanding.

97. **Not ours or not allowed:** not credited to us or disapproved.

98. **Hitting a grosser quality:** impressing those of duller mind or baser disposition; **cried up:** acclaimed; praised.

"The rough brake that virtue must go through." From Geoffrey Whitney, *A Choice of Emblems* (1586).
"Whereas the good do live amongst the bad;
And virtue grows where seed of vices springs;
The wicked sort to wound the good are glad;
And vices thrust at virtue all their stings."

16

Is named your wars in France. This makes bold
    mouths.
Tongues spit their duties out, and cold hearts freeze
Allegiance in them. Their curses now
Live where their prayers did; and it's come to pass,   75
This tractable obedience is a slave
To each incensed will. I would your Highness
Would give it quick consideration, for
There is no primer business.
   King.   By my life,   80
This is against our pleasure.
   Wol.   And for me,
I have no further gone in this than by
A single voice, and that not passed me but
By learned approbation of the judges. If I am   85
Traduced by ignorant tongues, which neither know
My faculties nor person yet will be
The chronicles of my doing, let me say
'Tis but the fate of place and the rough brake
That virtue must go through. We must not stint   90
Our necessary actions in the fear
To cope malicious censurers; which ever,
As rav'nous fishes, do a vessel follow
That is new trimmed but benefit no further
Than vainly longing. What we oft do best,   95
By sick interpreters, once weak ones, is
Not ours or not allowed; what worst, as oft,
Hitting a grosser quality, is cried up
For our best act. If we shall stand still,
In fear our motion will be mocked or carped at,   100

102. **State statues:** powerless symbols of governments.

105. **issue:** outcome.

108. **from:** contrary to.

109. **stick them in our will:** wound them according to our whim.

110. **trembling:** fearsome.

111. **lop:** lopped branch or branches.

114. **questioned:** disputed.

122. **Hardly conceive:** think badly; **noised:** rumored.

We should take root here where we sit or sit
State statues only.
 King.   Things done well,
And with a care, exempt themselves from fear;
Things done without example in their issue   105
Are to be feared. Have you a precedent
Of this commission? I believe, not any.
We must not rend our subjects from our laws
And stick them in our will. Sixth part of each?
A trembling contribution! Why, we take   110
From every tree, lop, bark, and part o' the timber,
And though we leave it with a root, thus hacked,
The air will drink the sap. To every county
Where this is questioned send our letters, with
Free pardon to each man that has denied   115
The force of this commission. Pray, look to't:
I put it to your care.
 Wol. [*To the Secretary*] A word with you.
Let there be letters writ to every shire
Of the King's grace and pardon. The grieved 120
  commons
Hardly conceive of me: let it be noised
That through our intercession this revokement
And pardon comes. I shall anon advise you
Further in the proceeding.   *Exit Secretary.* 125

Enter Surveyor.

 Queen. I am sorry that the Duke of Buckingham
Is run in your displeasure.

130. **bound:** obligated (for natural gifts).

132. **out of:** beyond.

136. **complete:** well endowed; accomplished.

140. **habits:** attire, with a possible pun on "customs."

145. **practices:** treasons.

154. **issue:** offspring.

King.   It grieves many:
The gentleman is learned and a most rare speaker;
To Nature none more bound; his training such   130
That he may furnish and instruct great teachers
And never seek for aid out of himself. Yet see,
When these so noble benefits shall prove
Not well disposed, the mind growing once corrupt,
They turn to vicious forms ten times more ugly   135
Than ever they were fair. This man so complete,
Who was enrolled 'mongst wonders, and when we,
Almost with ravished list'ning, could not find
His hour of speech a minute; he, my lady,
Hath into monstrous habits put the graces   140
That once were his and is become as black
As if besmeared in hell. Sit by us: you shall hear—
This was his gentleman in trust—of him
Things to strike honor sad. Bid him recount
The fore-recited practices; whereof   145
We cannot feel too little, hear too much.
      Wol. Stand forth and with bold spirit relate what
          you,
Most like a careful subject, have collected
Out of the Duke of Buckingham.   150
      King.   Speak freely.
      Sur. First, it was usual with him—every day
It would infect his speech—that if the King
Should without issue die he'll carry it so
To make the scepter his: these very words   155
I've heard him utter to his son-in-law,
Lord Aberga'ny, to whom by oath he menaced

161. **friended:** befriended; gratified.

168. **fail:** childless death.

171. **vain:** idle; **Nicholas Henton:** Nicholas Hopkins of Henton, according to Holinshed; see I.ii.262.

178. **the Rose:** Buckingham's manor in Candlewick Street.

184. **doubted:** feared.

Revenge upon the Cardinal.

Wol.   Please your Highness, note
This dangerous conception in this point.   160
Not friended by his wish, to your high person
His will is most malignant, and it stretches
Beyond you to your friends.

Queen.   My learned lord Cardinal,
Deliver all with charity.   165

King.   Speak on.
How grounded he his title to the crown
Upon our fail? To this point hast thou heard him
At any time speak aught?

Sur.   He was brought to this   170
By a vain prophecy of Nicholas Henton.

King. What was that Henton?

Sur.   Sir, a Chartreux friar,
His confessor, who fed him every minute
With words of sovereignty.   175

King.   How knowst thou this?

Sur. Not long before your Highness sped to France,
The Duke being at the Rose, within the parish
St. Lawrence Poultney, did of me demand
What was the speech among the Londoners   180
Concerning the French journey. I replied,
Men feared the French would prove perfidious,
To the King's danger. Presently the Duke
Said, 'twas the fear indeed, and that he doubted
'Twould prove the verity of certain words   185
Spoke by a holy monk; "that oft," says he,
"Hath sent to me, wishing me to permit

188. **choice hour:** suitable moment.

193. **demure confidence:** (1) modest boldness; (2) a manner serious and inspiring trust.

194. **pausingly:** in a measured manner.

199. **lost your office:** according to Holinshed, Buckingham's surveyor, Charles Knyvet, or Knevet, was so accused and dismissed and laid the false accusation against the Duke in revenge.

201. **spleen:** malice.

211. **forged him some design:** suggested to him a plan of action.

212. **much like:** very likely.

217. **rank:** presumptuous or rebellious.

John de la Car, my chaplain, a choice hour
To hear from him a matter of some moment:
Whom after under the confession's seal   190
He solemnly had sworn that what he spoke
My chaplain to no creature living but
To me should utter, with demure confidence
This pausingly ensued: neither the King nor's heirs,
Tell you the Duke, shall prosper. Bid him strive   195
To gain the love o' the commonalty. The Duke
Shall govern England."
   Queen.   If I know you well,
You were the Duke's surveyor and lost your office
On the complaint o' the tenants. Take good heed   200
You charge not in your spleen a noble person
And spoil your nobler soul. I say, take heed:
Yes, heartily beseech you.
   King.   Let him on.
Go forward.   205
   Sur.   On my soul, I'll speak but truth.
I told my lord the Duke, by the Devil's illusions
The monk might be deceived, and that 'twas danger-
   ous for him
To ruminate on this so far until   210
It forged him some design, which, being believed,
It was much like to do. He answered, "Tush,
It can do me no damage"; adding further,
That, had the King in his last sickness failed,
The Cardinal's and Sir Thomas Lovell's heads   215
Should have gone off.
   King.   Ha! what, so rank? Ah, ha!

229. **father:** Henry Stafford, 2d Duke of Buckingham, who rebelled against Richard III but was captured at Salisbury before he could join forces with Richmond. His request to see the King was denied and he was quickly beheaded.

232. **made semblance of his duty:** made a show of submission.

243. **mounting:** lifting.

Pepin. From Jean de Serres, *A General Inventory of the History of France* (1611).

There's mischief in this man. Canst thou say further?
  Sur. I can, my liege.
  King.   Proceed.   220
  Sur.   Being at Greenwich,
After your Highness had reproved the Duke
About Sir William Bulmer—
  King.   I remember
Of such a time: being my sworn servant,   225
The Duke retained him his. But on: what hence?
  Sur. "If," quoth he, "I for this had been committed,
As to the Tower I thought, I would have played
The part my father meant to act upon
The usurper Richard, who, being at Salisbury,   230
Made suit to come in's presence, which if granted,
As he made semblance of his duty, would
Have put his knife into him."
  King.   A giant traitor!
  Wol. Now, madam, may His Highness live in free- 235
    dom,
And this man out of prison?
  Queen.   God mend all!
  King. There's something more would out of thee:
    what sayst?   240
  Sur. After "the Duke his father," with the "knife,"
He stretched him, and with one hand on his dagger,
Another spread on's breast, mounting his eyes,
He did discharge a horrible oath, whose tenor
Was, were he evil used, he would outgo   245
His father by as much as a performance

248. **period:** end; final purpose.

249. **attached:** arrested.

250. **present:** immediate. Actually, Buckingham's execution took place in 1521, four years before the tax referred to in this scene.

253. **to the height:** in the highest degree.

▬▬▬▬▬▬▬▬▬▬▬▬▬▬▬▬▬▬▬

I.iii. Several courtiers discuss the current fad for French fashions that has spread in London since the expedition to France. Cardinal Wolsey, a lavish host, is giving a supper party, for which they all set out.

▬▬▬▬▬▬▬▬▬▬▬▬▬

2. **juggle:** trick.

3. **strange:** foreign; **mysteries:** peculiar actions.

9. **fit:** grimace; **shrewd:** extreme.

10. **directly:** unequivocally.

12. **Pepin:** 1st Carolingian King of the Franks, father of Charlemagne; **Clotharius:** seventh-century King of the Franks; **keep state so:** i.e., hold their noses so high (as a chair of state is raised from the floor).

13. **legs:** ceremonial bows, with a pun.

15-6. **spavin . . . springhalt:** diseases of horses that affected their gaits.

Does an irresolute purpose.

    King.   There's his period,
To sheathe his knife in us. He is attached;
Call him to present trial. If he may   250
Find mercy in the law, 'tis his; if none,
Let him not seek't of us. By day and night!
He's traitor to the height.

                             Exeunt.

Scene III. [London. An antechamber in the Palace.]

   Enter Lord Chamberlain and Lord Sands.

    Cham. Is't possible the spells of France should
      juggle
Men into such strange mysteries?

    Sands.   New customs,
Though they be never so ridiculous,   5
Nay, let 'em be unmanly, yet are followed.

    Cham. As far as I see, all the good our English
Have got by the late voyage is but merely
A fit or two o' the face; but they are shrewd ones;
For when they hold 'em, you would swear directly   10
Their very noses had been counselors
To Pepin or Clotharius, they keep state so.

    Sands. They have all new legs, and lame ones. One
      would take it,
That never saw 'em pace before, the spavin   15

17. **Death:** God's death, a common oath.

19. **worn out Christendom:** abandoned their Christianity.

22. **Faith:** truly.

24. **Court gate:** in Shakespeare's time, a gate of the Palace of Whitehall, which became the monarch's principal residence from the time Henry VIII seized it in 1530 after Wolsey's fall until it burned in 1691. All that now remains of the palace is the Inigo Jones banqueting house built in 1619-22.

27. **quarrels:** duels.

33. **remnants:** scraps.

34. **feather:** an ornamental detail that was overdone by those adopting French fashions.

35. **honorable points of ignorance:** follies regarded as points of honor.

36. **fights and fireworks:** duels and spectacles; **fireworks** may also refer to venereal infection, syphilis often being called "the French disease."

39. **tennis:** a sport imported from France; **tall stockings:** long stockings. In the second decade of the seventeenth century, although full, rounded breeches were still worn, it became fashionable to wear them without the canions that had formerly covered the thighs, necessitating longer stockings than had been usual.

40. **blistered:** swollen; **types:** signs.

41. **understand:** a punning reference to the way they clothed their underpinnings.

42. **pack:** be off.

And springhalt reigned among 'em.

    Cham.   Death! my lord,

Their clothes are after such a pagan cut to't

That, sure, th' have worn out Christendom.

              Enter Sir Thomas Lovell.

                              How now!   20

What news, Sir Thomas Lovell?

    Lov.   Faith, my lord,

I hear of none but the new proclamation

That's clapped upon the Court gate.

    Cham.   What is't for?   25

    Lov. The reformation of our traveled gallants,

That fill the court with quarrels, talk, and tailors.

    Cham. I'm glad 'tis there: now I would pray our
        monsieurs

To think an English courtier may be wise   30

And never see the Louvre.

    Lov.   They must either,

For so run the conditions, leave those remnants

Of fool and feather that they got in France,

With all their honorable points of ignorance   35

Pertaining thereunto, as fights and fireworks,

Abusing better men than they can be

Out of a foreign wisdom, renouncing clean

The faith they have in tennis and tall stockings,

Short blistered breeches, and those types of travel,   40

And understand again like honest men,

Or pack to their old playfellows. There, I take it,

43. **cum privilegio:** "with approval," a formula used to indicate a license to print.

44. **lewdness:** (1) ignorance; (2) lasciviousness.

45. **physic:** medicine.

47-8. **What a loss our ladies/ Will have of these trim vanities:** (1) how our ladies will miss these splendid nothings; (2) what a loss (of chastity) our ladies will have by these splendid nothings.

50. **whoresons:** rogues.

51. **speeding:** successful; **lay down:** seduce.

52. **has no fellow:** is incomparable.

57. **plain song:** an unadorned tune; i.e., plain speech.

58. **by'r Lady:** by the Virgin.

59. **Held current music:** considered acceptable.

61. **colt's tooth:** sweet tooth; taste for the ladies.

They may, *cum privilegio,* wear away
The lag end of their lewdness and be laughed at.
    Sands. 'Tis time to give 'em physic, their diseases   45
Are grown so catching.
    Cham.   What a loss our ladies
Will have of these trim vanities!
    Lov.   Ay, marry,
There will be woe indeed, lords. The sly whoresons   50
Have got a speeding trick to lay down ladies:
A French song and a fiddle has no fellow.
    Sands. The Devil fiddle 'em! I am glad they are
        going,
For, sure, there's no converting of 'em. Now   55
An honest country lord, as I am, beaten
A long time out of play, may bring his plain song,
And have an hour of hearing; and, by'r Lady,
Held current music too.
    Cham.   Well said, Lord Sands;   60
Your colt's tooth is not cast yet.
    Sands.   No, my lord;
Nor shall not, while I have a stump.
    Cham.   Sir Thomas,
Whither were you agoing?   65
    Lov.   To the Cardinal's:
Your lordship is a guest too.
    Cham.   Oh, 'tis true:
This night he makes a supper, and a great one,
To many lords and ladies. There will be   70
The beauty of this kingdom, I'll assure you.

77. **black:** wicked.
80. **liberal:** generous.
83. **stays:** awaits.
87. **comptrollers:** stewards.

⁞⁞

I.iv. Anne Bullen [Boleyn] and a party of ladies are welcomed to Wolsey's supper, while courtiers exchange ribald comments. As Wolsey greets them, a new arrival is announced by drum, trumpet, and cannon fire. A servant reports a party of strangers and Wolsey bids the Lord Chamberlain greet them, since he speaks French. Wolsey soon suspects that the masked party is headed by the King, who confirms his suspicion by unmasking. Henry dances with Anne; attracted, he leads her into supper.

Lov. That churchman bears a bounteous mind in-
  deed,
A hand as fruitful as the land that feeds us.
His dews fall everywhere.   75
  Cham.   No doubt he's noble:
He had a black mouth that said other of him.
  Sands. He may, my lord: has wherewithal. In him
Sparing would show a worse sin than ill doctrine.
Men of his way should be most liberal: 80
They are set here for examples.
  Cham.   True, they are so;
But few now give so great ones. My barge stays:
Your Lordship shall along. Come, good Sir Thomas,
We shall be late else, which I would not be,   85
For I was spoke to, with Sir Henry Guildford,
This night to be comptrollers.
  Sands.   I am your Lordship's.
                                    Exeunt.

Scene IV. [A hall in York Place, Westminster.]

*Hautboys. A small table under a state for the Cardi-
nal, a longer table for the guests. Then enter Anne
Bullen and divers other Ladies and Gentlemen as
guests, at one door; at another door, enter Sir Henry
                    Guildford.*

  Guil. Ladies, a general welcome from His Grace
Salutes ye all. This night he dedicates

13. **lay:** secular, worldly, with a sexual pun.

14. **a running banquet:** (1) a meal grabbed on the run; (2) a feast of love.

23. **afford it:** make it possible.

To fair content and you. None here, he hopes,
In all this noble bevy, has brought with her
One care abroad: he would have all as merry   5
As, first, good company, good wine, good welcome,
Can make good people.

Enter Lord Chamberlain, Lord Sands, and [Sir
Thomas] Lovell.

                    O my lord, y' are tardy.
The very thought of this fair company
Clapped wings to me.   10
  Cham.   You are young, Sir Harry Guildford.
  Sands. Sir Thomas Lovell, had the Cardinal
But half my lay thoughts in him, some of these
Should find a running banquet ere they rested,
I think would better please 'em. By my life,   15
They are a sweet society of fair ones.
  Lov. Oh, that your Lordship were but now con-
    fessor
To one or two of these!
  Sands.   I would I were: 20
They should find easy penance.
  Lov.   Faith, how easy?
  Sands. As easy as a down bed would afford it.
  Cham. Sweet ladies, will it please you sit? Sir Harry,
Place you that side. I'll take the charge of this.   25
His Grace is ent'ring. Nay, you must not freeze:
Two women placed together makes cold weather.
My Lord Sands, you are one will keep 'em waking:

38. **Well said:** well done.

39. **fairly:** (1) finely; (2) amidst beauty.

42. **cure:** those for whose (spiritual) welfare he is responsible.

43. **Let me alone:** you may trust my ability.

Ent. 43. **Hautboys:** oboes.

50. **may:** as may.

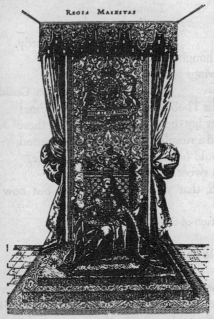

King James sitting in his state. From Thomas Milles, *The Catalogue of Honor* (1610).

Pray, sit between these ladies.

　　Sands.　　　　　　　　　By my faith,　　　　　30
And thank your Lordship. By your leave, sweet ladies.
If I chance to talk a little wild, forgive me;
I had it from my father.

　　Anne.　　　　　　　Was he mad, sir?

　　Sands. Oh, very mad, exceeding mad, in love too.　35
But he would bite none: just as I do now,
He would kiss you twenty with a breath. [*Kisses her.*]

　　Cham.　　　　　　　　　Well said, my lord.
So, now y' are fairly seated. Gentlemen,
The penance lies on you if these fair ladies　　　40
Pass away frowning.

　　Sands.　　　　　　For my little cure,
Let me alone.

Hautboys. Enter Cardinal Wolsey and takes his state.

　　Wol. Y' are welcome, my fair guests. That noble
　　　lady　　　　　　　　　　　　　　　　　　45
Or gentleman that is not freely merry
Is not my friend. This, to confirm my welcome;
And to you all, good health.　　　　　[*Drinks.*]

　　Sands.　　　　　　　Your Grace is noble:
Let me have such a bowl may hold my thanks　　50
And save me so much talking.

　　Wol.　　　　　　　My Lord Sands,
I am beholding to you. Cheer your neighbors.
Ladies, you are not merry. Gentlemen,

59. **gamester:** (1) sport; (2) wencher.

63. **thing:** another sexual innuendo.

SD 65. **chambers:** cannon.

72. **strangers:** foreigners.

75. **as:** like.

78-79. **the French tongue:** generally the language of the English Court and of diplomacy in Henry VIII's time, as well as in Shakespeare's. Wolsey himself could not speak French.

Whose fault is this?   55

   Sands.   The red wine first must rise
In their fair cheeks, my lord; then we shall have 'em
Talk us to silence.

   Anne.   You are a merry gamester,
My Lord Sands.   60

   Sands.   Yes, if I make my play.
Here's to your Ladyship: and pledge it, madam,
For 'tis to such a thing—

   Anne.   You cannot show me.

   Sands. I told your Grace they would talk anon.   65

           Drum and trumpet: chambers discharged.

   Wol.   What's that?

   Cham. Look out there, some of ye.   [*Exit Servant.*]

   Wol.   What warlike voice,
And to what end, is this? Nay, ladies, fear not;
By all the laws of war y' are privileged.   70

                Enter a Servant.

   Cham. How now! what is't?

   Serv.   A noble troop of strangers;
For so they seem. Th' have left their barge and
    landed;
And hither make, as great ambassadors   75
From foreign princes.

   Wol.   Good Lord Chamberlain,
Go, give 'em welcome: you can speak the French
    tongue.
And, pray, receive 'em nobly and conduct 'em   80

83. **broken:** (1) interrupted; (2) inadequate;
mend: improve.

89. **fame:** rumor.

93. **under your fair conduct:** by your gracious
allowance.

94. **Crave:** request; **leave:** permission.

97. **grace:** honor.

Into our presence, where this heaven of beauty
Shall shine at full upon them. Some attend him.
[*Exit Chamberlain, attended.*] *All rise, and tables
                                                    removed.*
You have now a broken banquet; but we'll mend it.
A good digestion to you all. And once more
I show'r a welcome on ye: welcome all.   85

*Hautboys. Enter King and others, as masquers,
habited like shepherds, ushered by the Lord Chamberlain. They pass directly before the Cardinal and
gracefully salute him.*

A noble company! what are their pleasures?
  Cham. Because they speak no English, thus they
      prayed
To tell your Grace, that, having heard by fame
Of this so noble and so fair assembly   90
This night to meet here, they could do no less,
Out of the great respect they bear to beauty,
But leave their flocks and, under your fair conduct,
Crave leave to view these ladies and entreat
An hour of revels with 'em.   95
  Wol.   Say, Lord Chamberlain,
They have done my poor house grace; for which I
      pay 'em
A thousand thanks and pray 'em take their pleasures.
            Choose Ladies, King and Anne Bullen.
  King. The fairest hand I ever touched! O beauty, 100
Till now I never knew thee!   *Music. Dance.*

106. **should:** must; **by his person:** i.e., his person betrays his identity.

107. **this place:** the chair of state he occupies.

117. **My royal choice:** my choice of royalty. Actually, Wolsey mistakenly picked out Sir Edward Neville, who resembled the King in build, to the amusement of the King and company.

121. **unhappily:** adversely.

123. **pleasant:** jovial.

130. **dainty:** choice.

Wol. My lord!

Cham. Your Grace?

Wol. Pray, tell 'em thus much from 105
me:

There should be one amongst 'em, by his person,
More worthy this place than myself; to whom,
If I but knew him, with my love and duty
I would surrender it.

Cham. I will, my lord. 110

Whispers [the Masquers].

Wol. What say they?

Cham. Such a one, they all confess,
There is indeed; which they would have your Grace
Find out, and he will take it.

Wol. Let me see then. 115

By all your good leaves, gentlemen: here I'll make
My royal choice.

King. [*Unmasking*] Ye have found him, Cardinal:
You hold a fair assembly! You do well, lord!
You are a churchman, or, I'll tell you, Cardinal, 120
I should judge now unhappily.

Wol. I am glad
Your Grace is grown so pleasant.

King. My Lord Chamber-
lain, 125

Prithee, come hither. What fair lady's that?

Cham. An't please your Grace, Sir Thomas Bullen's
daughter,
The Viscount Rochford, one of Her Highness' women.

King. By heaven, she is a dainty one. Sweetheart, 130

131. **were:** would be; **take you out:** dance with you.

146. **measure:** dance.

147. **again:** besides.

148. **knock it:** strike up.

I were unmannerly to take you out,
And not to kiss you. [*Kisses her.*] A health, gentle-
   men!
Let it go round.
   Wol. Sir Thomas Lovell, is the banquet ready   135
I' the privy chamber?
   Lov.   Yes, my lord.
   Wol.   Your Grace,
I fear, with dancing is a little heated.
   King. I fear, too much.   140
   Wol.   There's fresher air, my lord,
In the next chamber.
   King. Lead in your ladies, ev'ryone. Sweet partner,
I must not yet forsake you. Let's be merry.
Good my Lord Cardinal, I have half a dozen healths   145
To drink to these fair ladies and a measure
To lead 'em once again; and then let's dream
Who's best in favor. Let the music knock it.
                         Exeunt with trumpets.

THE FAMOUS HISTORY
OF THE LIFE OF
KING HENRY
THE EIGHTH

ACT II

II.i. Several gentlemen discuss Buckingham's trial. Despite an eloquent defense, his peers pronounced him guilty. The gentlemen agree that Wolsey is behind Buckingham's destruction; Wolsey is known to have a talent for getting rid of potential rivals for the King's favor. Buckingham, coming from his arraignment under guard, addresses the people and declares his innocence and loyalty to the King. He compares his fate with that of his father, executed by Richard III's order without a trial; he at least has been tried by his peers before being condemned. The gentlemen are moved by Buckingham's fate. One of them reveals a bit of news even more disturbing: the rumor that the King and Queen may separate. Cardinal Campeius has arrived as the Pope's representative in the matter. Wolsey is also believed to be responsible for this development in revenge because the Emperor, Katharine's nephew, did not give him the archbishopic of Toledo.

〰〰〰〰〰〰〰〰〰

17. **in a little:** in few words.

ACT II

⸻⸻⸻⸻⸻⸻⸻⸻⸻⸻⸻⸻⸻⸻⸻⸻⸻⸻⸻⸻⸻⸻⸻⸻⸻⸻⸻⸻⸻⸻⸻⸻⸻

Scene I. [A street in Westminster.]

Enter two Gentlemen at several doors.

1. Gent. Whither away so fast?
2. Gent. Oh, God save ye!
Ev'n to the Hall, to hear what shall become
Of the great Duke of Buckingham.
1. Gent.   I'll save you   5
That labor, sir. All's now done but the ceremony
Of bringing back the prisoner.
2. Gent.   Were you there?
1. Gent. Yes, indeed was I.
2. Gent.   Pray, speak what has happened.   10
1. Gent. You may guess quickly what.
2. Gent.   Is he found guilty?
1. Gent. Yes, truly is he, and condemned upon't.
2. Gent. I am sorry for't.
1. Gent.   So are a number more.   15
2. Gent. But, pray, how passed it?
1. Gent. I'll tell you in a little. The great Duke
Came to the bar, where, to his accusations

32

19. **still:** ever; i.e., to each accusation.
20. **sharp:** acute; telling; **reasons:** points.
24. **viva voce:** orally.
32. **fain:** willingly.
37. **Was either pitied in him or forgotten:** either seemed pitiful or made no impression.
43. **ill:** viciously.

He pleaded still not guilty and alleged
Many sharp reasons to defeat the law.   20
The King's attorney on the contrary
Urged on the examinations, proofs, confessions
Of divers witnesses; which the Duke desired
To have brought viva voce to his face.
At which appeared against him his surveyor;   25
Sir Gilbert Peck, his chancellor; and John Car,
Confessor to him; with that devil monk,
Hopkins, that made this mischief.

    2. Gent.   That was he
That fed him with his prophecies?   30
    1. Gent.   That same.
All these accused him strongly, which he fain
Would have flung from him, but indeed he could not.
And so his peers upon this evidence
Have found him guilty of high treason. Much   35
He spoke, and learnedly, for life, but all
Was either pitied in him or forgotten.

    2. Gent. After all this, how did he bear himself?

    1. Gent. When he was brought again to the bar, to
      hear   40
His knell rung out, his judgment, he was stirred
With such an agony he sweat extremely
And something spoke in choler, ill and hasty;
But he fell to himself again and sweetly
In all the rest showed a most noble patience.   45

    2. Gent. I do not think he fears death.

    1. Gent.   Sure, he does not;
He never was so womanish: the cause

51. **end:** ultimate cause.

53. **Kildare's attainder:** Gerald Fitzgerald, 9th Earl of Kildare, Lord Deputy of Ireland, 1513–1520, 1524, and 1532, was imprisoned in the Tower on charges of treason in 1533. Thus, it is evident that he was not attained for the purpose of installing Surrey as Lord Deputy, as Holinshed alleged.

55. **Earl Surrey:** Thomas Howard, Earl of Surrey, son of the Duke of Norfolk and son-in-law of Buckingham. Holinshed credits Wolsey with the device of sending him to Ireland so that he would not be at hand to aid his father-in-law.

58. **deep envious:** deeply hostile.

60. **requite:** pay it back in kind.

65. **perniciously:** so as to wish his utter destruction; **o':** on.

SD 71. **tipstaves:** officials of the court who had custody of the prisoner, armed with **tipstaves,** staffs symbolizing their function.

He may a little grieve at.

    2. Gent.   Certainly   50
The Cardinal is the end of this.

    1. Gent.   'Tis likely,
By all conjectures: first, Kildare's attainder,
Then deputy of Ireland; who removed,
Earl Surrey was sent thither, and in haste too,   55
Lest he should help his father.

    2. Gent.   That trick of state
Was a deep envious one.

    1. Gent.   At his return
No doubt he will requite it. This is noted,   60
And generally, whoever the King favors
The Cardinal instantly will find employment,
And far enough from Court too.

    2. Gent.   All the commons
Hate him perniciously, and, o' my conscience,   65
Wish him ten fathom deep. This Duke as much
They love and dote on, call him bounteous Bucking-
      ham,
The mirror of all courtesy—

    1. Gent.   Stay there, sir,   70
And see the noble ruined man you speak of.

*Enter Buckingham from his arraignment, Tipstaves
before him, the ax with the edge toward him, Hal-
berds on each side, accompanied with Sir Thomas
Lovell, Sir Nicholas Vaux, Sir William Sands, and
common people, etc.*

75. **lose:** forget.

78. **sink:** destroy; i.e., damn.

81. **upon the premises:** in view of the premised charges.

84. **look:** see to it.

85. **build their evils on the graves of great men:** advance their wicked careers by contriving the deaths of great men. It has been conjectured that **evils** has an undetermined special sense as used by Shakespeare here and in *Measure for Measure*, II.ii.212.

92. **only bitter to him, only dying:** bitter to him only (because of leaving them), dying alone.

95. **sacrifice:** propitiatory offering.

97. **charity:** Christian love.

99. **frankly:** freely; completely.

2. Gent. Let's stand close and behold him.

Buck.   All good people,
You that thus far have come to pity me,
Hear what I say, and then go home and lose me.   75
I have this day received a traitor's judgment
And by that name must die: yet, Heaven bear witness,
And if I have a conscience, let it sink me,
Even as the ax falls, if I be not faithful!
The law I bear no malice for my death;   80
'T has done upon the premises but justice:
But those that sought it I could wish more Christians.
Be what they will, I heartily forgive 'em.
Yet let 'em look they glory not in mischief,
Nor build their evils on the graves of great men;   85
For then my guiltless blood must cry against 'em.
For further life in this world I ne'er hope,
Nor will I sue, although the King have mercies
More than I dare make faults. You few that loved me
And dare be bold to weep for Buckingham,   90
His noble friends and fellows, whom to leave
Is only bitter to him, only dying,
Go with me, like good angels, to my end,
And, as the long divorce of steel falls on me,
Make of your prayers one sweet sacrifice   95
And lift my soul to Heaven. Lead on, o' God's name.

Lov. I do beseech your Grace, for charity,
If ever any malice in your heart
Were hid against me, now to forgive me frankly.

Buck. Sir Thomas Lovell, I as free forgive you   100
As I would be forgiven. I forgive all:

104. **envy:** enmity.

105. **Commend me:** give my respects to.

113. **fill up one monument:** will both be memorialized in his tomb.

114. **waterside:** i.e., to go by boat to the Tower of London.

119. **furniture:** accessories, such as cushions.

122. **state:** magnificence.

124. **Bohun:** the surname of his ancestress Eleanor Bohun, wife of Edward III's son, Thomas of Woodstock. The statement comes from Holinshed.

126. **seal:** certify.

129. **raised head:** raised a rebellious army.

131. **betrayed:** so Holinshed reported.

There cannot be those numberless offenses
'Gainst me that I cannot take peace with. No black
    envy
Shall mark my grave. Commend me to His Grace,   105
And if he speak of Buckingham, pray tell him
You met him half in Heaven. My vows and prayers
Yet are the King's and, till my soul forsake,
Shall cry for blessings on him. May he live
Longer than I have time to tell his years!   110
Ever beloved and loving may his rule be!
And when old time shall lead him to his end,
Goodness and he fill up one monument!
   Lov. To the waterside I must conduct your Grace
Then give my charge up to Sir Nicholas Vaux,   115
Who undertakes you to your end.
   Vaux.   Prepare there;
The Duke is coming. See the barge be ready,
And fit it with such furniture as suits
The greatness of his person.   120
   Buck.   Nay, Sir Nicholas,
Let it alone: my state now will but mock me.
When I came hither I was Lord High Constable
And Duke of Buckingham; now, poor Edward Bohun.
Yet I am richer than my base accusers,   125
That never knew what truth meant. I now seal it;
And with that blood will make 'em one day groan for't.
My noble father, Henry of Buckingham,
Who first raised head against usurping Richard,
Flying for succor to his servant Banister,   130
Being distressed, was by that wretch betrayed,

141. **happier:** more fortunate.
145. **end:** purpose.
148. **loose:** unrestrained.
150. **rub:** flaw.

And without trial fell. God's peace be with him!
Henry the Seventh succeeding, truly pitying
My father's loss, like a most royal prince,
Restored me to my honors and out of ruins   135
Made my name once more noble. Now his son,
Henry the Eighth, life, honor, name, and all
That made me happy at one stroke has taken
Forever from the world. I had my trial,
And must needs say, a noble one, which makes me   140
A little happier than my wretched father.
Yet thus far we are one in fortunes: both
Fell by our servants, by those men we loved most;
A most unnatural and faithless service!
Heaven has an end in all: yet, you that hear me,   145
This from a dying man receive as certain:
Where you are liberal of your loves and counsels
Be sure you be not loose; for those you make friends
And give your hearts to, when they once perceive
The least rub in your fortunes, fall away   150
Like water from ye, never found again
But where they mean to sink ye. All good people,
Pray for me! I must now forsake ye. The last hour
Of my long weary life is come upon me.
Farewell!   155
And when you would say something that is sad,
Speak how I fell. I have done; and God forgive me!
                    Exeunt Buckingham and Train.

   1. Gent. Oh, this is full of pity! Sir, it calls,
I fear, too many curses on their heads

163. **fall:** befall.

171. **confident:** certain (of your faith).

175. **held not:** did not continue.

177. **straight:** at once.

181. **found:** proved.

187. **Campeius:** Lorenzo Campeggio; he visited England to discuss the divorce in 1528.

That were the authors.   160
    2. Gent.   If the Duke be guiltless,
'Tis full of woe. Yet I can give you inkling
Of an ensuing evil, if it fall,
Greater than this.
    1. Gent. Good angels keep it from us!   165
What may it be? You do not doubt my faith, sir?
    2. Gent. This secret is so weighty, 'twill require
A strong faith to conceal it.
    1. Gent.   Let me have it:
I do not talk much.   170
    2. Gent. I am confident:
You shall, sir. Did you not of late days hear
A buzzing of a separation
Between the King and Katharine?
    1. Gent.   Yes, but it held not.   175
For when the King once heard it, out of anger
He sent command to the Lord Mayor straight
To stop the rumor and allay those tongues
That durst disperse it.
    2. Gent.   But that slander, sir,   180
Is found a truth now: for it grows again
Fresher than e'er it was, and held for certain
The King will venture at it. Either the Cardinal,
Or some about him near, have, out of malice
To the good Queen, possessed him with a scruple   185
That will undo her. To confirm this too,
Cardinal Campeius is arrived, and lately,
As all think, for this business.
    1. Gent.   'Tis the Cardinal;

198. **argue:** discuss.

‖‖‖

II.ii. King Henry is indeed considering a divorce from Katharine. He declares that he fears his marriage with his brother's widow is against the will of Heaven, though the Duke of Suffolk hints that love for another woman may have something to do with the King's scruples. Norfolk and Suffolk approach the King to divert him from his troublesome problem, but they are interrupted by the arrival of Campeius and Wolsey. Campeius reports that the Roman curia has selected him and Wolsey to judge the case of Henry's marriage. Henry vows that Queen Katharine shall have the best legal assistance and dispatches Gardiner, his secretary, to inform her of the imminent trial of the case. He orders Wolsey to arrange for the case to be heard in the Blackfriars.

‖‖

6. **main:** overmastering.

And merely to revenge him on the Emperor,   190
For not bestowing on him at his asking
The archbishopric of Toledo, this is purposed.
    2. Gent. I think you have hit the mark. But is't not
       cruel
That she should feel the smart of this? The Cardinal   195
Will have his will, and she must fall.
    1. Gent.   'Tis woeful.
We are too open here to argue this:
Let's think in private more.
                              Exeunt.

Scene II. [London. An antechamber in the Palace.]

Enter Lord Chamberlain, reading this letter.

Cham. "My lord, the horses your Lordship sent for,
with all the care I had, I saw well chosen, ridden, and
furnished. They were young and handsome and of the
best breed in the North. When they were ready to set
out for London, a man of my Lord Cardinal's, by   5
commission and main power, took 'em from me, with
this reason: his master would be served before a subject, if not before the King; which stopped our
mouths, sir."
I fear he will indeed. Well, let him have them.   10
He will have all, I think.

16. **sad:** grave.

18. **the marriage with his brother's wife:** Katharine was first married to Arthur, Henry VII's oldest son, who died in 1502, five months after they were married. A papal dispensation was necessary to permit Henry to marry his brother's widow, but Katharine claimed until her death that her marriage with Arthur had never been consummated.

24-5. **like the eldest son of Fortune,/ Turns what he list:** a reference to the concept that the goddess Fortune controlled men's fates by turning a wheel that raised or lowered them. She was often pictured as wearing a blindfold.

25. **know:** understand; detect.

26. **know himself:** i.e., know what it is to wield a king's true power, which Wolsey now usurps.

34. **for:** because of.

Enter to the Lord Chamberlain, the Dukes of Norfolk
and Suffolk.

Nor. Well met, my Lord Chamberlain.
Cham. Good day to both your Graces.
Suf. How is the King employed?
Cham.   I left him private,   15
Full of sad thoughts and troubles.
Nor.   What's the cause?
Cham. It seems the marriage with his brother's wife
Has crept too near his conscience.
Suf.   No, his conscience   20
Has crept too near another lady.
Nor.   'Tis so.
This is the Cardinal's doing, the King-Cardinal.
That blind priest, like the eldest son of Fortune,
Turns what he list. The King will know him one day.   25
Suf. Pray God he do! he'll never know himself else.
Nor. How holily he works in all his business!
And with what zeal! For, now he has cracked the
     league
Between us and the Emperor, the Queen's great   30
     nephew,
He dives into the King's soul and there scatters
Dangers, doubts, wringing of the conscience,
Fears, and despairs; and all these for his marriage.
And out of all these to restore the King,   35
He counsels a divorce, a loss of her
That, like a jewel, has hung twenty years

39. **with that excellence:** to the same superlative degree.

45. **These news:** originally a plural, meaning "new things."

46. **true:** honorable.

48. **The French king's sister:** Margaret, Duchess of Alençon, whom Wolsey for a time had in mind as a possible wife for Henry VIII.

49. **slept upon:** failed to see clearly.

57. **pitch:** shape.

60. **made without him:** not dependent upon him for position.

62. **breath:** airy nothing.

About his neck, yet never lost her luster;
Of her that loves him with that excellence
That angels love good men with; even of her   40
That, when the greatest stroke of fortune falls,
Will bless the King—and is not this course pious?
   Cham. Heaven keep me from such counsel! 'Tis
     most true
These news are everywhere, every tongue speaks 'em,   45
And every true heart weeps for't. All that dare
Look into these affairs see this main end,
The French king's sister. Heaven will one day open
The King's eyes, that so long have slept upon
This bold bad man.   50
   Suf.   And free us from his slavery.
   Nor. We had need pray,
And heartily, for our deliverance,
Or this imperious man will work us all
From princes into pages. All men's honors   55
Lie like one lump before him, to be fashioned
Into what pitch he please.
   Suf.   For me, my lords,
I love him not, nor fear him: there's my creed.
As I am made without him, so I'll stand,   60
If the King please. His curses and his blessings
Touch me alike: th' are breath I not believe in.
I knew him, and I know him: so I leave him
To him that made him proud, the Pope.
   Nor.   Let's in,   65
And with some other business put the King

83. **Malice ne'er meant:** not proceeding from deliberate spite.

84. **estate:** state; government.

87. **Go to:** be off.

88. **temporal:** worldly.

From these sad thoughts that work too much upon
    him.
My lord, you'll bear us company?
    Cham.   Excuse me: 70
The King has sent me otherwhere. Besides,
You'll find a most unfit time to disturb him.
Health to your Lordships.
    Nor.   Thanks, my good Lord Chamberlain.
         *Exit Lord Chamberlain; and the King draws the
                   curtain and sits reading pensively.*
    Suf. How sad he looks! Sure, he is much afflicted.   75
    King. Who's there, ha?
    Nor.   Pray God he be not angry.
    King. Who's there, I say? How dare you thrust
        yourselves
Into my private meditations?   80
Who am I? ha?
    Nor. A gracious King that pardons all offenses
Malice ne'er meant. Our breach of duty this way
Is business of estate, in which we come
To know your royal pleasure.   85
    King.   Ye are too bold.
Go to: I'll make ye know your times of business.
Is this an hour for temporal affairs, ha?

    Enter Wolsey and Campeius, with a commission.

Who's there? my good Lord Cardinal? O my Wolsey,
The quiet of my wounded conscience,   90

96. **found a talker:** proved one who talks rather than acts; see the proverb "Talkers are no good doers." The King urges Wolsey to see that his welcoming words are backed up by hospitality.

104. **sick:** corrupt; **for his place:** i.e., for all the dignity of his position.

107. **have-at-him:** challenge.

111. **voice:** vote.

115. **clerks:** scholars.

119. **One general tongue:** one man to speak for all the Roman clergy (the College of Cardinals).

Thou art a cure fit for a king. [*To Campeius*] You're welcome,
Most learned reverend sir, into our kingdom.
Use us and it. [*To Wolsey*] My good lord, have great care   95
I be not found a talker.
    Wol.   Sir, you cannot.
I would your Grace would give us but an hour
Of private conference.
    King. [*To Norfolk and Suffolk*] We are busy: go.   100
    Nor. [*Aside to Suffolk*] This priest has no pride in him!
    Suf. [*Aside to Norfolk*]   Not to speak of.
I would not be so sick though for his place:
But this cannot continue.   105
    Nor. [*Aside to Suffolk*] If it do,
I'll venture one have-at-him.
    Suf. [*Aside to Norfolk*]   I another.
                     Exeunt Norfolk and Suffolk.
    Wol. Your Grace has given a precedent of wisdom
Above all princes in committing freely   110
Your scruple to the voice of Christendom.
Who can be angry now? What envy reach you?
The Spaniard, tied by blood and favor to her,
Must now confess, if they have any goodness,
The trial just and noble. All the clerks,   115
I mean the learned ones, in Christian kingdoms
Have their free voices. Rome, the nurse of judgment,
Invited by your noble self, hath sent
One general tongue unto us, this good man,

130. **tender:** present; **virtue:** power.
134. **equal:** just.

This just and learned priest, Card'nal Campeius;   120
Whom once more I present unto your Highness.
　　King. And once more in mine arms I bid him wel-
　　　come
And thank the holy conclave for their loves.
They have sent me such a man I would have wished 125
　　for.
　　Cam. Your Grace must needs deserve all strangers'
　　　loves,
You are so noble. To your Highness' hand
I tender my commission, by whose virtue,   130
The Court of Rome commanding, you, My Lord
Cardinal of York, are joined with me their servant
In the unpartial judging of this business.
　　King. Two equal men. The Queen shall be ac-
　　　quainted   135
Forthwith for what you come. Where's Gardiner?
　　Wol. I know your Majesty has always loved her
So dear in heart not to deny her that
A woman of less place might ask by law,
Scholars allowed freely to argue for her.   140
　　King. Ay, and the best she shall have, and my favor
To him that does best. God forbid else. Cardinal,
Prithee, call Gardiner to me, my new Secretary.
I find him a fit fellow.　　　　　　　*[Exit Wolsey.]*

151. **Doctor Pace:** Richard Pace, whom Wolsey employed abroad in various diplomatic missions because his competence threatened his own pre-eminence with the King. In 1527 Wolsey had him imprisoned in the Tower, ostensibly for treason, but Pace was released before Wolsey's fall and outlived him by six years.

159. **stick:** hesitate.

161. **a foreign man still:** ever abroad.

166. **That good fellow:** i.e., Gardiner.

167. **appointment:** instruction.

168. **else:** otherwise.

169. **griped:** treated familiarly.

170. **modesty:** moderation; i.e., gently.

Thomas Wolsey at home. From M. Trentsentsky, *Costumes in Shakespeare's Historical Play of King Henry the Eighth* (n.d.).

Enter [Wolsey, with] Gardiner.

Wol. [*Aside to Gardiner*] Give me your hand. Much 145
    joy and favor to you:
You are the King's now.
    Gar. [*Aside to Wolsey*] But to be commanded
Forever by your Grace, whose hand has raised me.
    King. Come hither, Gardiner.   *Walks and whispers.* 150
    Cam. My Lord of York, was not one Doctor Pace
In this man's place before him?
    Wol.   Yes, he was.
    Cam. Was he not held a learned man?
    Wol.   Yes, surely. 155
    Cam. Believe me, there's an ill opinion spread then,
Even of yourself, Lord Cardinal.
    Wol.   How! of me?
    Cam. They will not stick to say you envied him,
And, fearing he would rise, he was so virtuous, 160
Kept him a foreign man still, which so grieved him
That he ran mad and died.
    Wol.   Heav'n's peace be with him!
That's Christian care enough. For living murmurers
There's places of rebuke. He was a fool, 165
For he would needs be virtuous. That good fellow,
If I command him, follows my appointment.
I will have none so near else. Learn this, brother,
We live not to be griped by meaner persons.
    King. Deliver this with modesty to the Queen. 170
                       Exit Gardiner.

171. **convenient:** appropriate.
172. **receipt:** accommodation.
174. **furnished:** arranged; outfitted.

‖‖‖‖‖‖‖‖‖‖‖‖‖‖‖‖‖‖‖‖‖‖‖‖‖‖‖‖‖‖‖‖‖‖‖‖‖

II.iii. An old lady of the Court quizzes Anne Bullen about the favor she has found with the King. Anne, distressed at rumors that Queen Katharine may be cast off by the King, stoutly declares that a low condition is much more fortunate than the cares of regal state. The old lady cannot believe that Anne would refuse to be a queen if she had the chance. The Lord Chamberlain informs Anne that the King has bestowed on her the title Marchioness of Pembroke, with an annual income of 1,000 pounds. The old lady predicts that this is only a token of the honors that are coming Anne's way, but Anne is ill at ease at the prospect.

‖‖‖‖‖‖‖‖‖‖‖‖‖‖‖‖‖‖‖‖‖‖‖‖‖‖‖‖‖‖‖

10. **process:** course of things.
11. **give her the avaunt:** send her packing.
13. **temper:** composition.

The most convenient place that I can think of
For such receipt of learning is Blackfriars:
There ye shall meet about this weighty business.
My Wolsey, see it furnished. O my lord,
Would it not grieve an able man to leave   175
So sweet a bedfellow? But, conscience, conscience!
Oh, 'tis a tender place; and I must leave her.

Exeunt.

Scene III. [London. An antechamber of the Queen's
apartments.]

Enter Anne Bullen and an Old Lady.

Anne. Not for that neither. Here's the pang that
    pinches:
His Highness having lived so long with her, and she
So good a lady that no tongue could ever
Pronounce dishonor of her—by my life,   5
She never knew harm doing!—Oh, now, after
So many courses of the sun enthroned,
Still growing in a majesty and pomp, the which
To leave a thousandfold more bitter than
'Tis sweet at first t' acquire—after this process,   10
To give her the avaunt, it is a pity
Would move a monster!
    Old La.   Hearts of most hard temper
Melt and lament for her.
    Anne.   Oh, God's will! much better   15

17. **quarrel, Fortune:** modern editors change the Folio's full stop after **quarrel** to a comma. If this apposition of **quarrel** and **Fortune** is what the author intended, fickle Fortune is conceived as a quarreler who inevitably falls out with her favorites.

18. **sufferance panging:** agony as painful.

21. **stranger:** foreigner. Anne's answer reflects the traditional custom of showing special courtesy to strangers; compare *Hamlet*, I.v.190.

25. **range:** rank.

26. **perked up:** (1) set on high; (2) decked out.

27. **golden sorrow:** golden crown that causes grief.

30. **troth:** faith.

31. **queen:** the old lady's reply puns on "quean," harlot.

32. **Beshrew me:** plague take me; a mild oath.

34. **spice:** although this can mean "taste," "dash," it also suggests camouflage, since spices were often used to cover the off taste of tainted meat.

35. **so:** such; **parts:** features.

37. **Affected:** desired.

38. **sooth:** truth.

39. **Saving your mincing:** for all your coyness; **capacity:** susceptibility.

40. **cheveril:** elastic, like kid leather.

She ne'er had known pomp. Though't be temporal,
Yet if that quarrel, Fortune, do divorce
It from the bearer, 'tis a sufferance panging
As soul and body's severing.

 Old La.   Alas, poor lady!   20
She's a stranger now again.

 Anne.   So much the more
Must pity drop upon her. Verily,
I swear 'tis better to be lowly born
And range with humble livers in content   25
Than to be perked up in a glist'ring grief
And wear a golden sorrow.

 Old La.   Our content
Is our best having.

 Anne.   By my troth and maidenhead, 30
I would not be a queen.

 Old La.   Beshrew me, I would,
And venture maidenhead for't; and so would you,
For all this spice of your hypocrisy.
You that have so fair parts of woman on you 35
Have too a woman's heart, which ever yet
Affected eminence, wealth, sovereignty;
Which, to say sooth, are blessings; and which gifts—
Saving your mincing—the capacity
Of your soft cheveril conscience would receive 40
If you might please to stretch it.

 Anne.   Nay, good troth.

 Old La. Yes, troth and troth! You would not be a
  queen?

 Anne. No, not for all the riches under Heaven. 45

46. **bowed:** bent, thus worthless.

52-3. **Pluck off a little:** i.e., come down from your high horse.

54-5. **I would not be a young count in your way/ For more than blushing comes to:** I would not remain a virgin like you longer than blushing takes.

56. **vouchsafe:** accept.

57. **get:** beget.

62. **emballing:** acceptance of the regal orb, with a ribald pun.

63. **'longed:** belonged.

69. **values not:** is not worth.

Costume of Anne Bullen. From M. Trentsentsky, *Costumes in Shakespeare's Historical Play of King Henry the Eighth* (n.d.).

48

Old La. 'Tis strange: a threepence bowed would
    hire me,
Old as I am, to queen it. But, I pray you,
What think you of a duchess? Have you limbs
To bear that load of title?   50
    Anne.   No, in truth.
    Old La. Then you are weakly made. Pluck off a
    little.
I would not be a young count in your way
For more than blushing comes to. If your back   55
Cannot vouchsafe this burden, 'tis too weak
Ever to get a boy.
    Anne.   How you do talk!
I swear again, I would not be a queen
For all the world.   60
    Old La.   In faith, for little England
You'ld venture an emballing. I myself
Would for Carnarvonshire, although there 'longed
No more to the crown but that. Lo, who comes here?

Enter Lord Chamberlain.

Cham. Good morrow, ladies, What were't worth to   65
    know
The secret of your conference?
    Anne.   My good lord,
Not your demand: it values not your asking.
Our mistress' sorrows we were pitying.   70
    Cham. It was a gentle business and becoming
The action of good women. There is hope

80. **Commends:** offers.

82. **Marchioness of Pembroke:** the title was not conferred until September 1, 1532, after Anne had become the King's mistress.

92. **Vouchsafe:** consent.

96. **approve the fair conceit:** confirm the good opinion.

All will be well.

  Anne.   Now, I pray God, amen!

  Cham. You bear a gentle mind, and heav'nly bless- **75**
   ings
Follow such creatures. That you may, fair lady,
Perceive I speak sincerely and high note's
Ta'en of your many virtues, the King's Majesty
Commends his good opinion of you to you and **80**
Does purpose honor to you no less flowing
Than Marchioness of Pembroke; to which title
A thousand pound a year annual support
Out of his grace he adds.

  Anne.   I do not know **85**
What kind of my obedience I should tender:
More than my all is nothing; nor my prayers
Are not words duly hallowed, nor my wishes
More worth than empty vanities. Yet prayers and
  wishes **90**
Are all I can return. Beseech your Lordship,
Vouchsafe to speak my thanks and my obedience,
As from a blushing handmaid, to His Highness,
Whose health and royalty I pray for.

  Cham.   Lady, **95**
I shall not fail t' approve the fair conceit
The King hath of you. [*Aside*] I have perused her
  well;
Beauty and honor in her are so mingled
That they have caught the King. And who knows yet **100**
But from this lady may proceed a gem
To lighten all this isle?—I'll to the King,

107. **courtier beggarly:** needy courtier; one who ever sues for favor without success.

108. **pat:** opportunely.

109. **suit of pounds:** profitable suit.

111. **compelled:** thrust upon her.

114. **Forty pence, no:** I'll bet forty pence it is not.

117. **mud:** rich soil; wealth.

118. **pleasant:** facetious.

119. **theme:** reason.

121. **pure respect:** sheer regard.

123. **mo:** additional.

128. **Make yourself mirth with your particular fancy:** amuse yourself with your private notions.

130. **salute my blood:** hearten me; **faints me:** makes me faint.

And say I spoke with you.
  Anne.   My honored lord.
          Exit Lord Chamberlain.
  Old La. Why, this it is: see, see!   105
I have been begging sixteen years in Court,
Am yet a courtier beggarly, nor could
Come pat betwixt too early and too late
For any suit of pounds; and you, O fate!
A very fresh fish here—fie, fie, fie upon   110
This compelled fortune!—have your mouth filled up
Before you open it.
  Anne.   This is strange to me.
  Old La. How tastes it? Is it bitter? Forty pence, no.
There was a lady once, 'tis an old story,   115
That would not be a queen, that would she not,
For all the mud in Egypt. Have you heard it?
  Anne. Come, you are pleasant.
  Old La.   With your theme, I could
O'ermount the lark. The Marchioness of Pembroke! 120
A thousand pounds a year for pure respect!
No other obligation! By my life,
That promises mo thousands. Honor's train
Is longer than his foreskirt. By this time
I know your back will bear a duchess. Say,   125
Are you not stronger than you were?
  Anne.   Good lady,
Make yourself mirth with your particular fancy
And leave me out on't. Would I had no being
If this salute my blood a jot: it faints me,   130
To think what follows.

133. **deliver:** report.

‖‖‖

II.iv. A hearing of the divorce case is convened
in a hall of the Blackfriars. Queen Katharine responds
to the crier's summons by kneeling to the King and
pleading that he not cast her off after twenty years
in which she has been a loving and devoted wife.
She points out that the legality of their marriage was
thoroughly weighed by wise counselors before it
was performed and begs that a decision be delayed
until she can have the assistance of advisers from
Spain. Wolsey and Campeius brush aside her request
for a delay. The Queen directly accuses Wolsey of
being her enemy and the one who first suggested
to Henry that he separate from her. Wolsey denies
responsibility. The Queen, turning to leave, ignores
the court crier's summons and declares that she will
not appear again in any court on the matter of
the divorce. The King has maintained an embarrassed
silence in the face of his wife's distress, but on her
departure he praises her wifely behavior during their
life together. At Wolsey's request, he denies that the
Cardinal prompted his examination of the validity
of his marriage and attributes it to a question raised
by the French ambassador about the legitimacy of
their daughter Mary. Katharine's failure to bear a
healthy son, he began to fear, might signify Heaven's
displeasure at their union. Campeius suggests that
the court adjourn and steps be taken to dissuade the
Queen from appealing to Rome.

‖‖‖‖‖‖‖‖‖‖‖‖‖‖‖‖‖‖‖‖‖‖‖‖‖‖‖‖‖‖‖‖‖‖‖‖‖

Ent. sennet: a ceremonial fanfare.

51

The Queen is comfortless and we forgetful
In our long absence. Pray, do not deliver
What here y' have heard to her.
    Old La.   What do you think me? 135
                                 Exeunt.

Scene IV. [London. A hall in Blackfriars.]

*Trumpets, sennet and cornets. Enter two Vergers, with
short silver wands; next them, two Scribes, in the habit
of Doctors; after them, the [Arch-]bishop of Canterbury alone; after him, the Bishops of Lincoln, Ely,
Rochester, and St. Asaph; next them, with some small
distance, follows a Gentleman bearing the Purse, with
the great Seal and a Cardinal's hat; then two Priests,
bearing each a Silver Cross; then a Gentleman-Usher
bareheaded, accompanied with a Sergeant at arms
bearing a Silver Mace; then two Gentlemen bearing
two great Silver Pillars; after them, side by side, the
two Cardinals; two Noblemen with the Sword and
Mace. The King takes place under the cloth of state;
the two Cardinals sit under him as judges. The Queen
takes place some distance from the King. The Bishops
place themselves on each side the Court, in manner
of a consistory; below them, the Scribes. The Lords
sit next the Bishops. The rest of the Attendants stand
in convenient order about the stage.*

Wol. Whilst our commission from Rome is read,

5. **allowed:** granted.
19. **indifferent:** impartial.
20. **equal:** just.
24. **your good grace:** both his affection and his person.

Let silence be commanded.
   King.   What's the need?
It hath already publicly been read,
And on all sides the authority allowed;   5
You may then spare that time.
   Wol.   Be't so. Proceed.
   Scribe. Say, Henry King of England, come into the
    court.
   Crier. Henry King of England, etc.   10
   King. Here.
   Scribe. Say, Katharine Queen of England, come into
    the court.
   Crier. Katharine Queen of England, etc.

*The Queen makes no answer, rises out of her chair,
goes about the court, comes to the King, and kneels
at his feet; then speaks.*

   Queen. Sir, I desire you do me right and justice 15
And to bestow your pity on me; for
I am a most poor woman, and a stranger,
Born out of your dominions; having here
No judge indifferent, nor no more assurance
Of equal friendship and proceeding. Alas, sir,   20
In what have I offended you? What cause
Hath my behavior given to your displeasure
That thus you should proceed to put me off,
And take your good grace from me? Heaven witness
I have been to you a true and humble wife,   25
At all times to your will conformable,

34. **derived:** drawn.

39. **many children:** Mary was the only surviving child; all the others were stillborn or died soon after birth.

43. **Against:** toward.

Ever in fear to kindle your dislike,
Yea, subject to your countenance, glad or sorry
As I saw it inclined. When was the hour
I ever contradicted your desire,   30
Or made it not mine too? Or which of your friends
Have I not strove to love, although I knew
He were mine enemy? What friend of mine
That had to him derived your anger did I
Continue in my liking? nay, gave notice   35
He was from thence discharged? Sir, call to mind
That I have been your wife in this obedience
Upward of twenty years, and have been blest
With many children by you. If in the course
And process of this time you can report,   40
And prove it too, against mine honor aught,
My bond to wedlock, or my love and duty,
Against your sacred person, in God's name,
Turn me away and let the foul'st contempt
Shut door upon me, and so give me up   45
To the sharp'st kind of justice. Please you, sir,
The King, your father, was reputed for
A prince most prudent, of an excellent
And unmatched wit and judgment. Ferdinand,
My father, King of Spain, was reckoned one   50
The wisest prince that there had reigned by many
A year before. It is not to be questioned
That they had gathered a wise council to them
Of every realm, that did debate this business,
Who deemed our marriage lawful. Wherefore I   55
    humbly

62. **of your choice:** as chosen by you.

65. **bootless:** useless.

66. **That longer you desire the court:** that you ask the court to delay.

85. **potent circumstances:** powerful evidence.

Beseech you, sir, to spare me till I may
Be by my friends in Spain advised, whose counsel
I will implore. If not, i' the name of God,
Your pleasure be fulfilled! 60
   Wol.   You have here, lady,
And of your choice, these reverend fathers, men
Of singular integrity and learning,
Yea, the elect o' the land, who are assembled
To plead your cause. It shall be therefore bootless 65
That longer you desire the court, as well
For your own quiet, as to rectify
What is unsettled in the King.
   Cam.   His Grace
Hath spoken well and justly: therefore, madam, 70
It's fit this royal session do proceed,
And that, without delay, their arguments
Be now produced and heard.
   Queen.   Lord Cardinal,
To you I speak. 75
   Wol.   Your pleasure, madam?
   Queen.   Sir,
I am about to weep; but, thinking that
We are a queen, or long have dreamed so, certain
The daughter of a king, my drops of tears 80
I'll turn to sparks of fire.
   Wol.   Be patient yet.
   Queen. I will, when you are humble: nay, before,
Or God will punish me. I do believe,
Induced by potent circumstances, that 85
You are mine enemy, and make my challenge

90. **abhor:** shrink from; reject.

96. **stood to:** maintained; **charity:** Christian forbearance.

100. **spleen:** malice.

107. **gainsay:** contradict; **wound:** punish.

110. **free:** innocent.

The Bishop of Rochester in ceremonial attire. From M. Trentsentsky, *Costumes in Shakespeare's Historical Play of King Henry the Eighth* (n.d.).

You shall not be my judge. For it is you
Have blown this coal betwixt my lord and me,
Which God's dew quench! Therefore I say again,
I utterly abhor, yea, from my soul   90
Refuse you for my judge, whom, yet once more,
I hold my most malicious foe and think not
At all a friend to truth.

   Wol.   I do profess
You speak not like yourself, who ever yet   95
Have stood to charity and displayed the effects
Of disposition gentle, and of wisdom
O'ertopping woman's pow'r. Madam, you do me
   wrong.
I have no spleen against you, nor injustice   100
For you or any. How far I have proceeded,
Or how far further shall, is warranted
By a commission from the Consistory,
Yea, the whole Consistory of Rome. You charge me
That I have blown this coal. I do deny it.   105
The King is present: if it be known to him
That I gainsay my deed, how may he wound,
And worthily, my falsehood! Yea, as much
As you have done my truth. If he know
That I am free of your report, he knows   110
I am not of your wrong. Therefore in him
It lies to cure me; and the cure is to
Remove these thoughts from you: the which before
His Highness shall speak in, I do beseech
You, gracious madam, to unthink your speaking   115

121. **sign:** certify; i.e., he signifies himself a churchman by his pretended meekness and humility; **seeming:** appearance.

125. **slightly:** easily.

126. **pow'rs are your retainers:** powerful men serve you.

126-28. **your words,/ Domestics to you, serve your will as't please/ Yourself pronounce their office:** i.e., what you wish is no sooner said than done.

129. **tender:** cherish.

136. **Stubborn:** rebellious.

143. **note:** heed; **keep your way:** keep on going.

And to say so no more.

   Queen.   My lord, my lord,
I am a simple woman, much too weak
T' oppose your cunning. Y' are meek and humble-
   mouthed;   120
You sign your place and calling, in full seeming,
With meekness and humility; but your heart
Is crammed with arrogancy, spleen, and pride.
You have, by fortune and His Highness' favors,
Gone slightly o'er low steps and now are mounted 125
Where pow'rs are your retainers and your words,
Domestics to you, serve your will as't please
Yourself pronounce their office. I must tell you,
You tender more your person's honor than
Your high profession spiritual; that again   130
I do refuse you for my judge and here,
Before you all, appeal unto the Pope
To bring my whole cause 'fore His Holiness,
And to be judged by him.

         She curtsies to the King, and offers to depart.

   Cam.   The Queen is obstinate,   135
Stubborn to justice, apt to accuse it, and
Disdainful to be tried by't. 'Tis not well.
She's going away.

   King. Call her again.

   Crier. Katharine Queen of England, come into the 140
   court.

   Gent. Ush. Madam, you are called back.

   Queen. What need you note it? Pray you, keep your
   way.

153. **alone:** matchless.

155. **government:** conduct.

156. **Obeying in commanding:** obedience to command.

156-57. **parts/ Sovereign and pious else:** i.e., other supreme and pious qualities.

157. **speak thee out:** describe you truly.

162. **require:** request.

167. **broach:** open.

169. **question on't:** consideration of it.

171. **one the least word:** the slightest word.

When you are called, return. Now the Lord help!   145
They vex me past my patience. Pray you, pass on.
I will not tarry, no, nor ever more
Upon this business my appearance make
In any of their courts.

> *Exeunt Queen and her Attendants.*

  King.   Go thy ways, Kate: 150
That man i' the world who shall report he has
A better wife, let him in nought be trusted
For speaking false in that. Thou art alone,
If thy rare qualities, sweet gentleness,
Thy meekness saintlike, wifelike government,   155
Obeying in commanding, and thy parts
Sovereign and pious else could speak thee out,
The queen of earthly queens. She's noble born,
And like her true nobility she has
Carried herself toward me.   160

  Wol.   Most gracious sir,
In humblest manner I require your Highness
That it shall please you to declare in hearing
Of all these ears—for where I am robbed and bound,
There must I be unloosed, although not there   165
At once and fully satisfied—whether ever I
Did broach this business to your Highness or
Laid any scruple in your way which might
Induce you to the question on't or ever
Have to you, but with thanks to God for such   170
A royal lady, spake one the least word that might
Be to the prejudice of her present state

173. **touch:** hurt.

175. **I do excuse you:** historians have never determined the precise degree of Wolsey's responsibility for putting the idea of divorce into Henry's head, but Wolsey did all he could to make the divorce possible until he came to the unhappy realization that Anne Bullen would be Katharine's successor.

181. **justified:** excused.

186. **speak:** attest.

193. **French ambassador:** Holinshed reports this, but it seems to be a fabrication by Wolsey. The marriage projected in 1527 was to be between Francis I and Princess Mary. The French ambassador in question was the Bishop of Tarbes.

197. **determinate:** final.

199. **advertise:** inform.

202. **Sometimes:** formerly.

Or touch of her good person?
 King.   My Lord Cardinal,
I do excuse you; yea, upon mine honor,   175
I free you from't. You are not to be taught
That you have many enemies that know not
Why they are so, but, like to village curs,
Bark when their fellows do. By some of these
The Queen is put in anger. Y' are excused.   180
But will you be more justified? You ever
Have wished the sleeping of this business, never de-
  sired
It to be stirred, but oft have hindered, oft,
The passages made toward it. On my honor,   185
I speak my good Lord Card'nal to this point,
And thus far clear him. Now, what moved me to't,
I will be bold with time and your attention.
Then mark the inducement. Thus it came: give heed
  to't.   190
My conscience first received a tenderness,
Scruple, and prick on certain speeches uttered
By the Bishop of Bayonne, then French ambassador,
Who had been hither sent on the debating
A marriage 'twixt the Duke of Orleans and   195
Our daughter Mary. I' the progress of this business,
Ere a determinate resolution, he,
I mean the Bishop, did require a respite,
Wherein he might the King his lord advertise
Whether our daughter were legitimate,   200
Respecting this our marriage with the dowager,
Sometimes our brother's wife. This respite shook

205. **forced such way:** made such forcible progress.

206. **mazed:** confused.

213. **Or:** either.

217. **gladded in't:** made glad by the provision of an heir to the throne.

219. **my issue's fail:** my failure to have children.

220. **hulling:** floating.

225. **yet not well:** i.e., and is not yet well.

229. **under my oppression I did reek:** my distress caused me to sweat.

230. **moved you:** mentioned it to you.

The Bishop of Lincoln in ceremonial attire. From M. Trentsentsky, *Costumes in Shakespeare's Historical Play of King Henry the Eighth* (n.d.).

The bottom of my conscience, entered me,
Yea, with a splitting power, and made to tremble
The region of my breast; which forced such way   205
That many mazed considerings did throng
And pressed in with this caution. First, methought
I stood not in the smile of Heaven, who had
Commanded nature that my lady's womb,
If it conceived a male-child by me, should   210
Do no more offices of life to't than
The grave does to the dead; for her male issue
Or died where they were made or shortly after
This world had aired them. Hence I took a thought
This was a judgment on me, that my kingdom,   215
Well worthy the best heir o' the world, should not
Be gladded in't by me. Then follows that
I weighed the danger which my realms stood in
By this my issue's fail; and that gave to me
Many a groaning throe. Thus hulling in   220
The wild sea of my conscience, I did steer
Toward this remedy whereupon we are
Now present here together: that's to say,
I meant to rectify my conscience, which
I then did feel full sick and yet not well,   225
By all the reverend fathers of the land
And doctors learned. First I began in private
With you, my Lord of Lincoln: you remember
How under my oppression I did reek
When I first moved you.   230
    Lin.   Very well, my liege.
    King. I have spoke long. Be pleased yourself to say

237. **consequence of dread:** dreadful consequence.

237-38. **committed/ The daring'st counsel which I had to doubt:** applied to your doubt the most daring counsel I could think of.

245-46. **by particular consent proceeded/ Under your hands and seals:** proceeded by unanimous consent, attested by your signatures and seals.

252. **wear our mortal state to come with her:** live with her for the rest of our life.

253. **before:** rather than; **primest:** most preeminent.

254. **paragoned:** acclaimed a paragon.

258. **earnest motion:** pressing appeal.

How far you satisfied me.

    Lin.   So please your Highness,

The question did at first so stagger me,   235

Bearing a state of mighty moment in't

And consequence of dread, that I committed

The daring'st counsel which I had to doubt,

And did entreat your Highness to this course

Which you are running here.   240

    King.   I then moved you,

My Lord of Canterbury, and got your leave

To make this present summons. Unsolicited

I left no reverend person in this court

But by particular consent proceeded   245

Under your hands and seals. Therefore, go on;

For no dislike i' the world against the person

Of the good Queen, but the sharp thorny points

Of my alleged reasons, drives this forward.

Prove but our marriage lawful, by my life   250

And kingly dignity, we are contented

To wear our mortal state to come with her,

Katharine our queen, before the primest creature

That's paragoned o' the world.

    Cam.   So please your Highness, 255

The Queen being absent, 'tis a needful fitness

That we adjourn this court till further day.

Meanwhile must be an earnest motion

Made to the Queen to call back her appeal

She intends unto His Holiness.   260

    King. [*Aside*]   I may perceive

These Cardinals trifle with me. I abhor

This dilatory sloth and tricks of Rome.
My learned and well-beloved servant, Cranmer,
Prithee, return: with thy approach, I know,　　265
My comfort comes along.—Break up the court.
I say, set on.

Exeunt in manner as they entered.

THE FAMOUS HISTORY
OF THE LIFE OF
KING HENRY
THE EIGHTH

ACT III

III.i. Queen Katharine is visited by Wolsey and Campeius. They assure her of their devotion to her interests. But when Campeius suggests that she be ruled by the King's wishes rather than insist upon a legal decision, she flares up and accuses them of hypocrisy. The two cardinals soothe her and gain her consent to present their advice.

⁞⁞⁞⁞⁞⁞⁞⁞⁞⁞⁞⁞⁞⁞⁞⁞⁞⁞⁞⁞⁞⁞⁞⁞⁞⁞⁞⁞

12. **lay by:** rested.

ACT III

Scene I. [London. The Queen's apartments.]

The Queen and her Women, as at work.

Queen. Take thy lute, wench. My soul grows sad
  with troubles:
Sing and disperse 'em, if thou canst. Leave working.

Song

Orpheus with his lute made trees
And the mountaintops that freeze   5
  Bow themselves when he did sing.
To his music plants and flowers
Ever sprung, as sun and showers
  There had made a lasting spring.

Everything that heard him play,   10
Even the billows of the sea,
  Hung their heads and then lay by.
In sweet music is such art,
Killing care and grief of heart
  Fall asleep, or hearing die.   15

16. **How now:** what's this.

19. **presence:** reception room.

28. **all hoods make not monks:** proverbial: *Cucullus non facit monachum;* i.e., clerical garb is no proof of holiness.

30-31. **part of a housewife:** something of a housewife. Holinshed describes the Queen and her women as employed in needlework when the Cardinals visited her.

32. **would be:** would like to be; **against:** before.

Enter a Gentleman.

Queen. How now!

Gent. And't please your Grace, the two great
  Cardinals
Wait in the presence.

    Queen. Would they speak with me? 20

    Gent. They willed me say so, madam.

    Queen. Pray their Graces
To come near. [*Exit Gentleman.*] What can be their
  business
With me, a poor weak woman, fall'n from favor? 25
I do not like their coming. Now I think on't,
They should be good men, their affairs as righteous.
But all hoods make not monks.

Enter the two Cardinals, Wolsey and Campeius.

Wol. Peace to your Highness!

    Queen. Your Graces find me here part of a house- 30
  wife:
I would be all, against the worst may happen.
What are your pleasures with me, reverend lords?

    Wol. May it please you, noble madam, to withdraw
Into your private chamber, we shall give you 35
The full cause of our coming.

    Queen. Speak it here:
There's nothing I have done yet, o' my conscience,
Deserves a corner. Would all other women

46. **that way I am wife in:** concerning my status as a wife.

48-9. **Tanta est erga te mentis integritas, regina serenissima:** such is my integrity of mind toward you, O most serene queen.

51. **truant:** poor scholar.

63. **all faith:** only loyalty.

Could speak this with as free a soul as I do!   40
My lords, I care not, so much I am happy
Above a number, if my actions
Were tried by ev'ry tongue, ev'ry eye saw 'em,
Envy and base opinion set against 'em,
I know my life so even. If your business   45
Seek me out, and that way I am wife in,
Out with it boldly: truth loves open dealing.

> *Wol. Tanta est erga te mentis integritas, regina*
>   *serenissima—*

> *Queen.* O good my lord, no Latin;   50
I am not such a truant since my coming,
As not to know the language I have lived in.
A strange tongue makes my cause more strange, sus-
     picious.
Pray speak in English. Here are some will thank you,   55
If you speak truth, for their poor mistress' sake.
Believe me, she has had much wrong. Lord Cardinal,
The willing'st sin I ever yet committed
May be absolved in English.

> *Wol.*   Noble lady,   60
I am sorry my integrity should breed,
And service to His Majesty and you,
So deep suspicion, where all faith was meant.
We come not by the way of accusation
To taint that honor every good tongue blesses,   65
Nor to betray you any way to sorrow—
You have too much, good lady—but to know
How you stand minded in the weighty difference
Between the King and you, and to deliver,

74. **still:** always.

75. **late:** recent.

76. **far:** extreme; perhaps with the sense "erroneous."

89. **her sake that I have been:** i.e., for the sake of what I have been, the Queen of England.

90. **last fit:** death throes.

Wolsey in street attire. From M. Trentsentsky, *Costumes in Shakespeare's Historical Play of King Henry the Eighth* (n.d.).

Like free and honest men, our just opinions   70
And comforts to your cause.
    Cam.   Most honored madam,
My Lord of York, out of his noble nature,
Zeal and obedience he still bore your Grace,
Forgetting, like a good man, your late censure   75
Both of his truth and him, which was too far,
Offers, as I do, in a sign of peace,
His service and his counsel.
    Queen. [*Aside*]   To betray me.—
My lords, I thank you both for your good wills.   80
Ye speak like honest men; pray God, ye prove so!
But how to make ye suddenly an answer,
In such a point of weight, so near mine honor,
More near my life, I fear, with my weak wit,
And to such men of gravity and learning,   85
In truth, I know not. I was set at work
Among my maids, full little, God knows, looking
Either for such men or such business.
For her sake that I have been—for I feel
The last fit of my greatness—good your Graces,   90
Let me have time and counsel for my cause.
Alas, I am a woman, friendless, hopeless!
    Wol. Madam, you wrong the King's love with these
       fears.
Your hopes and friends are infinite.   95
    Queen.   In England
But little for my profit. Can you think, lords,
That any Englishman dare give me counsel?
Or be a known friend, 'gainst His Highness' pleasure—

100. **grown so desperate to be honest:** become so rash as to speak the truth.

102. **weigh out:** remedy.

103. **grow to:** rely on.

107. **griefs:** grievances.

124. **hollow:** insincere.

126. **cordial:** comfort.

127. **lost:** destroyed; **among:** between.

Though he be grown so desperate to be honest—   100
And live a subject? Nay, forsooth, my friends,
They that must weigh out my afflictions,
They that my trust must grow to, live not here.
They are, as all my other comforts, far hence
In mine own country, lords.   105

    Cam.   I would your Grace
Would leave your griefs and take my counsel.

    Queen.   How, sir?

    Cam. Put your main cause into the King's protec-
        tion: 110
He's loving and most gracious. 'Twill be much
Both for your honor better and your cause;
For if the trial of the law o'ertake ye,
You'll part away disgraced.

    Wol.   He tells you rightly.   115

    Queen. Ye tell me what ye wish for both, my ruin.
Is this your Christian counsel? Out upon ye!
Heaven is above all yet: there sits a judge
That no king can corrupt.

    Cam.   Your rage mistakes us.   120

    Queen. The more shame for ye. Holy men I thought
        ye,
Upon my soul, two reverend cardinal virtues;
But cardinal sins and hollow hearts I fear ye.
Mend 'em, for shame, my lords. Is this your comfort?   125
The cordial that ye bring a wretched lady,
A woman lost among ye, laughed at, scorned?
I will not wish ye half my miseries:
I have more charity. But say, I warned ye;

130. **at once:** sometime.

132. **mere distraction:** downright madness.

133. **envy:** hostility.

135. **false professors:** professors of false sentiments.

137. **churchmen's habits:** i.e., religious men only in attire.

138. **sick:** feeble.

139. **has:** elliptical for "he has."

141-42. **all the fellowship I hold now with him/ Is only my obedience:** i.e., I can be like a wife to him now only in showing obedience.

143-44. **All your studies/ Make me a curse like this:** my wretched state is the result of your schemes and plots.

145. **worse:** i.e., than her actual situation. See the proverb "Foolish fear doubles danger."

146. **speak:** defend.

147. **no friends:** a reflection of the proverb "He dwells far from neighbors that is fain to praise himself."

150. **with all my full affections:** whole-heartedly.

151. **Still:** always; **met:** complied with (his wishes).

153. **superstitious:** devoted to the point of idolatry.

Take heed, for Heaven's sake, take heed, lest at once 130
The burden of my sorrows fall upon ye.

Wol. Madam, this is a mere distraction:
You turn the good we offer into envy.

Queen. Ye turn me into nothing. Woe upon ye,
And all such false professors! Would you have me— 135
If you have any justice, any pity,
If ye be anything but churchmen's habits—
Put my sick cause into his hands that hates me?
Alas, has banished me his bed already,
His love, too long ago! I am old, my lords, 140
And all the fellowship I hold now with him
Is only my obedience. What can happen
To me above this wretchedness? All your studies
Make me a curse like this.

Cam.   Your fears are worse. 145

Queen. Have I lived thus long—let me speak myself,
Since virtue finds no friends—a wife, a true one?
A woman, I dare say without vainglory,
Never yet branded with suspicion?
Have I with all my full affections 150
Still met the King? loved him next Heav'n? obeyed
    him?
Been, out of fondness, superstitious to him?
Almost forgot my prayers to content him?
And am I thus rewarded? 'Tis not well, lords. 155
Bring me a constant woman to her husband,
One that ne'er dreamed a joy beyond his pleasure,
And to that woman, when she has done most,
Yet will I add an honor, a great patience.

168. **angels' faces:** referring to the comment of St. Gregory the Great on the beauty of Anglo-Saxon youths whom he saw sold at Rome, which inspired him to send missionaries to convert their heathen countrymen.

171. **poor wenches:** referring to her Spanish attendants.

178. **ends:** intentions.

184-85. **utterly/ Grow from the King's acquaintance:** lose the King's friendship completely.

185. **carriage:** behavior.

187. **stubborn:** rebellious.

Wol. Madam, you wander from the good we aim at. 160
Queen. My lord, I dare not make myself so guilty
To give up willingly that noble title
Your master wed me to. Nothing but death
Shall e'er divorce my dignities.
Wol.   Pray, hear me. 165
Queen. Would I had never trod this English earth
Or felt the flatteries that grow upon it!
Ye have angels' faces, but Heaven knows your hearts.
What will become of me now, wretched lady!
I am the most unhappy woman living. 170
Alas, poor wenches, where are now your fortunes?
Shipwracked upon a kingdom, where no pity,
No friends, no hope; no kindred weep for me;
Almost no grave allowed me! Like the lily,
That once was mistress of the field and flourished, 175
I'll hang my head and perish.
Wol.   If your Grace
Could but be brought to know our ends are honest,
You'ld feel more comfort. Why should we, good lady,
Upon what cause, wrong you? Alas, our places, 180
The way of our profession is against it.
We are to cure such sorrows, not to sow 'em.
For goodness' sake, consider what you do;
How you may hurt yourself, ay, utterly
Grow from the King's acquaintance, by this carriage. 185
The hearts of princes kiss obedience,
So much they love it, but to stubborn spirits
They swell and grow as terrible as storms.
I know you have a gentle, noble temper,

200. **studies:** endeavors.
204. **wit:** wisdom.
206. **do:** offer.

A soul as even as a calm: pray think us   190
Those we profess, peace makers, friends, and servants.
  Cam. Madam, you'll find it so. You wrong your
    virtues
With these weak women's fears. A noble spirit,
As yours was put into you, ever casts   195
Such doubts, as false coin, from it. The King loves
    you:
Beware you lose it not. For us, if you please
To trust us in your business, we are ready
To use our utmost studies in your service.   200
  Queen. Do what ye will, my lords: and pray forgive
    me
If I have used myself unmannerly.
You know I am a woman, lacking wit
To make a seemly answer to such persons.   205
Pray do my service to His Majesty.
He has my heart yet and shall have my prayers
While I shall have my life. Come, reverend fathers,
Bestow your counsels on me. She now begs
That little thought, when she set footing here,   210
She should have bought her dignities so dear.
                        Exeunt.

III.ii. Norfolk, Suffolk, Surrey, and the Lord
Chamberlain gossip about the prospect of Wolsey's
downfall. His letters to the Pope attempting to
interfere with the divorce have come to King Henry's
eyes. The Lord Chamberlain reports that Wolsey's
effort to undermine Anne Bullen are too late: she
and the King are already married and preparations
are under way for her coronation. Cranmer has
returned from Europe with the opinions of university
scholars confirming the King's view about the divorce
from Katharine. Very soon the marriage with Anne
Bullen and the coronation will be announced, and
Katharine will be titled Princess Dowager rather
than Queen of England. Wolsey, disturbed at the
prospect of Anne becoming Queen, ponders ways
to prevent it. He is unaware that he has accidentally
included an inventory of his wealth among papers
sent to the King. The revelation of Wolsey's worldly
goods prompts the King to question his loyalty. At
the end of their interview, the King hands Wolsey
the inventory and the letters to the Pope; Wolsey
now realizes that he is a ruined man. He is ordered
to give up the Great Seal to Norfolk and the other
lords and to remove himself to Esher House in
Surrey. When Wolsey refuses to relinquish the Seal
to anyone except the King himself, the lords go
off to report this to Henry, leaving Wolsey to reflect
on the uncertain fate of those who trust to royal
favor. Cromwell tells him that Sir Thomas More has
already been chosen Lord Chancellor, that Cranmer
has been made Archbishop of Canterbury, and that

Scene II. [London. Antechamber of the King's apartment.]

*Enter the Duke of Norfolk, Duke of Suffolk, [Earl of]
Surrey, and Lord Chamberlain.*

Nor. If you will now unite in your complaints
And force them with a constancy, the Cardinal
Cannot stand under them. If you omit
The offer of this time, I cannot promise
But that you shall sustain mo new disgraces,   5
With these you bear already.
Sur.   I am joyful
To meet the least occasion that may give me
Remembrance of my father-in-law, the Duke,
To be revenged on him.   10
Suf.   Which of the peers
Have uncontemned gone by him, or at least
Strangely neglected? When did he regard
The stamp of nobleness in any person
Out of himself?   15
Cham.   My lords, you speak your pleasures.
What he deserves of you and me I know;
What we can do to him, though now the time
Gives way to us, I much fear. If you cannot
Bar his access to the King, never attempt   20
Anything on him, for he hath a witchcraft
Over the King in's tongue.
Nor.   Oh, fear him not:

the King and Anne Bullen have been secretly married. Wolsey attributes his ruin to Anne, but he urges Cromwell to take warning from his example, to beware of ambition, and to devote himself to the service of God and his country.

iiiiiiiiiiiiiiiiiiiiiiiiiiiiiiiiiiiiii

Ent. **Norfolk:** historically, this scene treats events in 1529, but the Duke of Norfolk of the earlier scenes died in 1524, at which time Surrey succeeded as Duke.

2. **force:** urge; **with a constancy:** firmly.

3. **omit:** neglect.

4. **time:** opportunity.

5. **mo:** other; **disgraces:** troubles.

12. **uncontemned gone by him:** avoided his (Wolsey's) contempt.

13. **Strangely neglected:** been coldly ignored.

15. **Out of:** other than; beyond.

19. **Gives way:** is opportune; **fear:** doubt.

24. **out:** over.

27. **come off:** escape.

32. **contrary proceedings:** disliking the prospect of Henry's marrying Anne Bullen, Wolsey appealed to the Pope to order Henry to part from her.

36. **practices:** plots.

45. **creature:** subordinate; waitingwoman.

50-51. **coasts/ And hedges his own way:** pursues his own course in a stealthy manner.

51. **in this point:** i.e., in regard to the King's relations with Anne Bullen.

52-3. **he brings his physic/ After his patient's death:** proverbial.

71

Hath married the fair lady.

   Sur.   Would he had!   55

  Suf. May you be happy in your wish, my lord!
For, I profess, you have it.

   Sur.   Now, all my joy

Trace the conjunction!

   Suf.   My amen to't!   60

   Nor.   All men's!

  Suf. There's order given for her coronation.
Marry, this is yet but young and may be left
To some ears unrecounted. But, my lords,
She is a gallant creature and complete   65
In mind and feature. I persuade me, from her
Will fall some blessing to this land which shall
In it be memorized.

   Sur.   But will the King
Digest this letter of the Cardinal's?   70
The Lord forbid!

   Nor.   Marry, amen!

   Suf.   No, no!
There be mo wasps that buzz about his nose
Will make this sting the sooner. Cardinal Campeius 75
Is stol'n away to Rome; hath ta'en no leave;
Has left the cause o' the King unhandled and
Is posted as the agent of our Cardinal
To second all his plot. I do assure you
The King cried "Ha!" at this.   80

   Cham.   Now God incense him,
And let him cry "Ha!" louder!

   Nor.   But, my lord,

85. **is returned in his opinions:** Cranmer had suggested that the King secure favorable opinions from English and European universities on the King's wish to divorce his brother's widow; he himself polled the German universities. The passage apparently means "has returned with the opinions he sought."

106. **Presently:** immediately.

108. **a heed:** concern.

When returns Cranmer?

Suf. He is returned in his opinions, which   85
Have satisfied the King for his divorce,
Together with all famous colleges
Almost in Christendom. Shortly, I believe,
His second marriage shall be published and
Her coronation. Katharine no more   90
Shall be called Queen but Princess Dowager
And widow to Prince Arthur.

Nor.   This same Cranmer's
A worthy fellow and hath ta'en much pain
In the King's business.   95

Suf.   He has, and we shall see him
For it an archbishop.

Nor.   So I hear.

Suf.   'Tis so.
The Cardinal!   100

Enter Wolsey and Cromwell.

Nor.   Observe, observe, he's moody.

Wol. The packet, Cromwell,
Gave't you the King?

Crom.   To his own hand, in's bedchamber.

Wol. Looked he o' the inside of the paper?   105

Crom.   Presently
He did unseal them, and the first he viewed,
He did it with a serious mind; a heed
Was in his countenance. You he bade

112. **abroad:** forth from his chamber.

129. **This candle burns not clear:** i.e., Anne is an unworthy match for the King. Perhaps there is some connection with the proverb "Choose neither women nor linen by candlelight." But compare *Cymbeline*, I.vi.130-33: "by peeping in an eye/ Base and illustrious as the smoky light/ That's fed with stinking tallow."

132. **spleeny:** fervid.

134. **hard-ruled:** self-willed.

FRANCESCO I·RE DE FRANCIA

Francis I, King of France. From Pompilio Totti, *Ritratti et elogii di capitani illustri* (1635).

74

Attend him here this morning.   110
  Wol.   Is he ready
To come abroad?
  Crom.   I think by this he is.
  Wol. Leave me awhile.   *Exit Cromwell.*
[*Aside*] It shall be to the Duchess of Alençon,   115
The French king's sister: he shall marry her.
Anne Bullen! No, I'll no Anne Bullens for him.
There's more in't than fair visage. Bullen!
No, we'll no Bullens. Speedily I wish
To hear from Rome. The Marchioness of Pembroke!   120
  Nor. He's discontented.
  Suf.   May be he hears the King
Does whet his anger to him.
  Sur.   Sharp enough,
Lord, for thy justice!   125
  Wol. [*Aside*] The late Queen's gentlewoman, a
    knight's daughter,
To be her mistress' mistress! The Queen's Queen!
This candle burns not clear: 'tis I must snuff it;
Then out it goes. What though I know her virtuous   130
And well deserving? Yet I know her for
A spleeny Lutheran and not wholesome to
Our cause that she should lie i' the bosom of
Our hard-ruled King. Again, there is sprung up
An heretic, an arch one, Cranmer, one   135
Hath crawled into the favor of the King,
And is his oracle.
  Nor.   He is vexed at something.

141. **on's:** of his.

152. **straight:** instantly.

154-55. **casts/ His eye against the moon:** literally, looks skyward, but there was a proverbial saying about casting beyond the moon, meaning to make wild conjectures.

158. **mutiny:** conflict.

160. **wot you:** do you know.

161. **on my conscience:** I would swear to it.

162. **thus importing:** concerning the following. This detail is taken from material in Holinshed concerning Thomas Ruthall, Bishop of Durham, who accidentally sent such an inventory to Wolsey.

163. **several parcels:** individual pieces; **plate:** silverware.

165. **at such proud rate:** so magnificent; **outspeaks:** exceeds.

Sur. I would 'twere something that would fret the
    string,   140
The master-cord on's heart!

Enter King, reading of a schedule, [and Lovell].

Suf.   The King, the King!
  King. What piles of wealth hath he accumulated
To his own portion! and what expense by the hour
Seems to flow from him! How, i' the name of thrift,   145
Does he rake this together? Now, my lords,
Saw you the Cardinal?
  Nor.   My lord, we have
Stood here observing him. Some strange commotion
Is in his brain. He bites his lip and starts;   150
Stops on a sudden, looks upon the ground,
Then lays his finger on his temple; straight
Springs out into fast gait; then stops again,
Strikes his breast hard, and anon he casts
His eye against the moon. In most strange postures   155
We have seen him set himself.
  King.   It may well be:
There is a mutiny in's mind. This morning
Papers of state he sent me to peruse,
As I required; and wot you what I found   160
There, on my conscience, put unwittingly?
Forsooth, an inventory, thus importing,
The several parcels of his plate, his treasure,
Rich stuffs, and ornaments of household, which
I find at such proud rate that it outspeaks   165

179-80. the inventory/ Of your best graces: the King is deliberately ambiguous; Wolsey will have no suspicion that the King really refers to the costly belongings in the inventory he did not mean the King to see.

184. ill husband: careless accountant.

185. my companion: the King claims to be equally careless of worldly concerns.

191. amongst my brethren mortal: i.e., mortal like the rest of mankind.

192. tendance: attention.

Possession of a subject.

Nor.　　　　　　It's Heaven's will.
Some spirit put this paper in the packet
To bless your eye withal.

King.　　　　　　If we did think　　　　170
His contemplation were above the earth
And fixed on spiritual object, he should still
Dwell in his musings: but I am afraid
His thinkings are below the moon, not worth
His serious considering.　　　　　　175

King takes his seat; whispers Lovell, who goes to the
*　　　　　　　　　　　　　　　　　　Cardinal.*

Wol.　　　　　　Heaven forgive me!
Ever God bless your Highness!

King.　　　　　　　　Good my lord,
You are full of heavenly stuff and bear the inventory
Of your best graces in your mind; the which　　180
You were now running o'er. You have scarce time
To steal from spiritual leisure a brief span
To keep your earthly audit. Sure, in that
I deem you an ill husband and am glad
To have you therein my companion.　　　　185

Wol.　　　　　　　　Sir,
For holy offices I have a time; a time
To think upon the part of business which
I bear i' the state; and nature does require
Her times of preservation, which perforce　　190
I, her frail son, amongst my brethren mortal,
Must give my tendance to.

King.　　　　　　You have said well.

195. **lend:** offer.

195-96. **my doing well/ With my well saying:** cf. the proverb " 'Tis better to do well than to say well." See also II.ii.87.

200. **crown:** fulfill.

202. **alone:** only.

204. **havings:** income.

215. **studied purposes:** painstaking efforts.

218. **filed:** marched alongside; equaled.

223. **render:** return; **allegiant:** loyal.

Wol. And ever may your Highness yoke together,
As I will lend you cause, my doing well   195
With my well saying!

King.   'Tis well said again;
And 'tis a kind of good deed to say well.
And yet words are no deeds. My father loved you.
He said he did and with his deed did crown   200
His word upon you. Since I had my office
I have kept you next my heart; have not alone
Employed you where high profits might come home
But pared my present havings to bestow
My bounties upon you.   205

Wol. [*Aside*]   What should this mean?

Sur. [*Aside*] The Lord increase this business!

King.   Have I not made you
The prime man of the state? I pray you, tell me,
If what I now pronounce you have found true;   210
And, if you may confess it, say withal,
If you are bound to us or no. What say you?

Wol. My sovereign, I confess your royal graces,
Show'red on me daily, have been more than could
My studied purposes requite; which went   215
Beyond all man's endeavors. My endeavors
Have ever come too short of my desires,
Yet filed with my abilities. Mine own ends
Have been mine so that evermore they pointed
To the good of your most sacred person and   220
The profit of the state. For your great graces
Heaped upon me, poor undeserver, I
Can nothing render but allegiant thanks,

229-30. **The honor of it/ Does pay the act of it:** i.e., the virtue of loyalty is repaid by the honor that virtue receives.

231. **foulness:** ignominy.

236. **bond of duty:** i.e., his obligation to the Pope as his legate.

237. **As 'twere in love's particular:** as a matter of personal affection.

242. **duty:** devotion.

246. **chiding:** angry.

250. **breast:** heart.

251. **open't:** reveal it.

My pray'rs to Heaven for you, my loyalty,
Which ever has and ever shall be growing,   225
Till death, that winter, kill it.
   King.   Fairly answered:
A loyal and obedient subject is
Therein illustrated. The honor of it
Does pay the act of it; as, i' the contrary,   230
The foulness is the punishment. I presume
That, as my hand has opened bounty to you,
My heart dropped love, my pow'r rained honor, more
On you than any; so your hand and heart,
Your brain and every function of your power,   235
Should, notwithstanding that your bond of duty,
As 'twere in love's particular, be more
To me, your friend, than any.
   Wol.   I do profess
That for your Highness' good, I ever labored   240
More than mine own: that am, have, and will be—
Though all the world should crack their duty to you
And throw it from their soul, though perils did
Abound, as thick as thought could make 'em, and
Appear in forms more horrid—yet my duty,   245
As doth a rock against the chiding flood,
Should the approach of this wild river break
And stand unshaken yours.
   King.   'Tis nobly spoken.
Take notice, lords, he has a loyal breast,   250
For you have seen him open't. [*Giving him papers*]
   Read o'er this;
And, after, this: and then to breakfast with

259. **galled:** wounded.
260. **makes him nothing:** destroys him.
262. **accompt:** account.
265. **fee:** pay.
266. **cross:** unfriendly.
267. **main:** mighty.
271. **take right:** come off; succeed.
272. **bring me off:** rescue me.
278. **exhalation:** meteor.

What appetite you have.

Exit King, frowning upon the Cardinal: the nobles
      throng after him, smiling and whispering.

  Wol.   What should this mean?   255
What sudden anger's this? How have I reaped it?
He parted frowning from me, as if ruin
Leaped from his eyes. So looks the chafed lion
Upon the daring huntsman that has galled him;
Then makes him nothing. I must read this paper: 260
I fear, the story of his anger. 'Tis so!
This paper has undone me: 'tis the accompt
Of all that world of wealth I have drawn together
For mine own ends; indeed, to gain the popedom
And fee my friends in Rome. O negligence,   265
Fit for a fool to fall by! What cross devil
Made me put this main secret in the packet
I sent the King? Is there no way to cure this?
No new device to beat this from his brains?
I know 'twill stir him strongly; yet I know   270
A way, if it take right, in spite of fortune,
Will bring me off again. What's this? "To the Pope!"
The letter, as I live, with all the business
I writ to's Holiness. Nay then, farewell!
I have touched the highest point of all my greatness;   275
And, from that full meridian of my glory,
I haste now to my setting. I shall fall
Like a bright exhalation in the evening
And no man see me more.

284. **Asher House:** actually, Esher House, in Surrey, which Wolsey had begged from Richard Fox, Bishop of Winchester.

296. **wanton:** insolent.

300. **In time will find:** i.e., their **envious courses** will find.

305. **letters patents:** documents of authorization.

Enter to Wolsey the Dukes of Norfolk and Suffolk,
the Earl of Surrey, and the Lord Chamberlain.

Nor. Hear the King's pleasure, Cardinal: who com- 280
    mands you
To render up the Great Seal presently
Into our hands and to confine yourself
To Asher House, my Lord of Winchester's,
Till you hear further from His Highness.   285
    Wol.   Stay.
Where's your commission? Lords, words cannot carry
Authority so weighty.
    Suf.   Who dare cross 'em,
Bearing the King's will from his mouth expressly?   290
    Wol. Till I find more than will or words to do it—
I mean your malice—know, officious lords,
I dare and must deny it. Now I feel
Of what coarse metal ye are molded—envy!
How eagerly ye follow my disgraces,   295
As if it fed ye! And how sleek and wanton
Ye appear in everything may bring my ruin!
Follow your envious courses, men of malice:
You have Christian warrant for 'em, and, no doubt,
In time will find their fit rewards. That seal   300
You ask with such a violence the King,
Mine and your master, with his own hand gave me;
Bade me enjoy it, with the place and honors,
During my life; and, to confirm his goodness,
Tied it by letters patents. Now, who'll take it?   305

313. **scarlet:** referring to his cardinal's scarlet gown.

317. **Weighed:** equaled in worth.

320. **gavest him:** accused him of.

324. **talking:** prating.

333. **mate:** vie with.

Sur. The King, that gave it.

Wol. It must be himself, then.

Sur. Thou art a proud traitor, priest.

Wol. Proud lord, thou liest.

Within these forty hours Surrey durst better   310
Have burnt that tongue than said so.

Sur. Thy ambition,
Thou scarlet sin, robbed this bewailing land
Of noble Buckingham, my father-in-law.
The heads of all thy brother Cardinals,   315
With thee and all thy best parts bound together,
Weighed not a hair of his. Plague of your policy!
You sent me deputy for Ireland;
Far from his succor, from the King, from all
That might have mercy on the fault thou gavest him;   320
Whilst your great goodness, out of holy pity,
Absolved him with an ax.

Wol. This, and all else
This talking lord can lay upon my credit,
I answer, is most false. The Duke by law   325
Found his deserts. How innocent I was
From any private malice in his end,
His noble jury and foul cause can witness.
If I loved many words, lord, I should tell you
You have as little honesty as honor,   330
That in the way of loyalty and truth
Toward the King, my ever royal master,
Dare mate a sounder man than Surrey can be
And all that love his follies.

Sur. By my soul,   335

340. **jaded:** treated contemptuously.

342. **dare:** terrify; **like larks:** i.e., as larks were bewildered and tricked into entering nets.

353. **issues:** posterity.

355. **articles:** itemized charges.

356. **Collected:** noted.

357. **sacring bell:** the bell rung to summon the parish to morning service.

363. **thus much:** i.e., I can say this much about them.

Your long coat, priest, protects you; thou shouldst feel
My sword i' the lifeblood of thee else. My lords,
Can ye endure to hear this arrogance?
And from this fellow? If we live thus tamely,
To be thus jaded by a piece of scarlet,   340
Farewell nobility! Let His Grace go forward,
And dare us with his cap like larks.

    Wol.   All goodness
Is poison to thy stomach.

    Sur.   Yes, that goodness   345
Of gleaning all the land's wealth into one,
Into your own hands, Card'nal, by extortion;
The goodness of your intercepted packets
You writ to the Pope against the King. Your goodness,
Since you provoke me, shall be most notorious.   350
My Lord of Norfolk, as you are truly noble,
As you respect the common good, the state
Of our despised nobility, our issues,
Who, if he live, will scarce be gentlemen,
Produce the grand sum of his sins, the articles   355
Collected from his life. I'll startle you
Worse than the sacring bell, when the brown wench
Lay kissing in your arms, Lord Cardinal.

    Wol. How much, methinks, I could despise this
      man,   360
But that I am bound in charity against it!

    Nor. Those articles, my lord, are in the King's hand:
But, thus much, they are foul ones.

    Wol.   So much fairer
And spotless shall mine innocence arise   365

366. **truth:** honesty.

373. **objections:** accusations.

374. **want:** lack.

375-76. **Have at you:** on guard.

378. **wrought:** contrived.

381. **Ego et Rex meus:** the correct Latin construction, but interpreted as typical of Wolsey's arrogance.

390. **allowance:** approval.

392-93. **caused/ Your holy hat to be stamped on the King's coin:** the archbishops of York and Canterbury both had the power to strike coins; where Wolsey presumed was in issuing groats, as well as the half-groats and halfpennies he was authorized to strike.

394-95. **substance:** money.

When the King knows my truth.

    Sur.　　　　　　　　　　This cannot save you.
I thank my memory, I yet remember
Some of these articles and out they shall.
Now, if you can blush and cry "guilty," Cardinal,　　370
You'll show a little honesty.

    Wol.　　　　　　　　　Speak on, sir:
I dare your worst objections. If I blush,
It is to see a nobleman want manners.

    Sur. I had rather want those than my head. Have at 375
      you!
First, that without the King's assent or knowledge
You wrought to be a legate, by which power
You maimed the jurisdiction of all bishops.

    Nor. Then, that in all you writ to Rome, or else　　380
To foreign princes, *Ego et Rex meus*
Was still inscribed; in which you brought the King
To be your servant.

    Suf.　　　　　　Then, that without the knowledge
Either of King or Council, when you went　　385
Ambassador to the Emperor, you made bold
To carry into Flanders the Great Seal.

    Sur. Item, you sent a large commission
To Gregory de Cassado, to conclude,
Without the King's will or the state's allowance,　　390
A league between His Highness and Ferrara.

    Suf. That out of mere ambition, you have caused
Your holy hat to be stamped on the King's coin.

    Sur. Then, that you have sent innumerable sub-
      stance—　　　　　　　　　　395

397-98. **prepare the ways/ You have for digni-ties:** i.e., bribe his way to the papal throne, to which he aspired.

398. **mere:** downright.

404. **open:** exposed.

407. **I forgive him:** i.e., it suits me to see him lowered.

411. **compass:** range; **praemunire:** the Statute of Praemunire forbade appealing from the King's courts to Rome and bringing bulls or other papal provisions into the kingdom. Wolsey's activities as papal legate, which the King had previously winked at, brought him within the scope of the statute.

413. **tenements:** dwellings.

414. **Chattels:** movable property.

By what means got, I leave to your own conscience—
To furnish Rome and to prepare the ways
You have for dignities, to the mere undoing
Of all the kingdom. Many more there are,
Which, since they are of you and odious,　　　　　400
I will not taint my mouth with.

 Cham.   O my lord!
Press not a falling man too far: 'tis virtue.
His faults lie open to the laws: let them,
Not you, correct him. My heart weeps to see him　405
So little of his great self.

 Sur.   I forgive him.

 Suf. Lord Cardinal, the King's further pleasure is—
Because all those things you have done of late,
By your power legatine within his kingdom,　　　410
Fall into the compass of a praemunire—
That therefore such a writ be sued against you,
To forfeit all your goods, lands, tenements,
Chattels, and whatsoever, and to be
Out of the King's protection. This is my charge.　415

 Nor. And so we'll leave you to your meditations
How to live better. For your stubborn answer
About the giving back the Great Seal to us,
The King shall know it, and, no doubt, shall thank you.
So fare you well, my little good Lord Cardinal.　420

       Exeunt all but Wolsey.

 Wol. So farewell to the little good you bear me.
Farewell! a long farewell to all my greatness!
This is the state of man: today he puts forth
The tender leaves of hopes; tomorrow blossoms

425. **blushing:** blooming.
427. **easy:** confident.
430. **wanton:** playful.
435. **rude:** rough.
440. **aspect:** glance; **ruin:** power to ruin.
446. **amazed:** dumbstruck; speechless.
448. **and:** if.

THOMAS MORVS QVONDAM SVPREMVS
TOTIVS ANGLIÆ CANCELLARIVS DIGNISS.
Hic est ille THOMAS *plebis de puluere magnus,*
Qui tulit intanum principis ira caput. A

Sir Thomas More. From Henry Holland, *Herwologia* [1620].

And bears his blushing honors thick upon him; 425
The third day comes a frost, a killing frost,
And, when he thinks, good easy man, full surely
His greatness is aripening, nips his root,
And then he falls, as I do. I have ventured,
Like little wanton boys that swim on bladders, 430
This many summers in a sea of glory,
But far beyond my depth. My high-blown pride
At length broke under me and now has left me,
Weary and old with service, to the mercy
Of a rude stream that must forever hide me. 435
Vain pomp and glory of this world, I hate ye!
I feel my heart new opened. Oh, how wretched
Is that poor man that hangs on princes' favors!
There is, betwixt that smile we would aspire to,
That sweet aspect of princes, and their ruin, 440
More pangs and fears than wars or women have:
And when he falls, he falls like Lucifer,
Never to hope again.

Enter Cromwell, standing amazed.

                              Why, how now, Cromwell!
Crom. I have no power to speak, sir. 445
Wol.   What, amazed
At my misfortunes? Can thy spirit wonder
A great man should decline? Nay, and you weep,
I am fall'n indeed.
Crom.   How does your Grace? 450
Wol.   Why, well;

468. **heaviest:** saddest.

469. **your displeasure with the King:** i.e., the King's displeasure with him.

Never so truly happy, my good Cromwell.
I know myself now, and I feel within me
A peace above all earthly dignities,
A still and quiet conscience. The King has cured me, 455
I humbly thank His Grace; and from these shoulders,
These ruined pillars, out of pity, taken
A load would sink a navy, too much honor.
Oh, 'tis a burden, Cromwell, 'tis a burden
Too heavy for a man that hopes for Heaven! 460
 Crom. I am glad your Grace has made that right
  use of it.
 Wol. I hope I have. I am able now, methinks,
Out of a fortitude of soul I feel,
To endure more miseries and greater far 465
Than my weak-hearted enemies dare offer.
What news abroad?
 Crom.   The heaviest and the worst
Is your displeasure with the King.
 Wol.   God bless him! 470
 Crom. The next is that Sir Thomas More is chosen
Lord Chancellor in your place.
 Wol.   That's somewhat sudden:
But he's a learned man. May he continue
Long in His Highness' favor and do justice 475
For truth's sake and his conscience; that his bones,
When he has run his course and sleeps in blessings,
May have a tomb of orphans' tears wept on him!
What more?
 Crom. That Cranmer is returned with welcome, 480
Installed Lord Archbishop of Canterbury.

486. **voice:** talk.
490. **gone beyond me:** deserted me.
491. **In:** because of.
501. **hopeful:** promising.

Fortunæ speculum CROMWELLVS *scandit ad alta*
Vt casu grauiore ruat, Regisque fauore
Tollitur que cadit liuore oppressus iniquæ

Thomas Cromwell. From Henry Holland, *Herwologia* [1620].

Wol. That's news indeed.

Crom.   Last, that the Lady Anne,
Whom the King hath in secrecy long married,
This day was viewed in open as his queen,   485
Going to chapel; and the voice is now
Only about her coronation.

  Wol. There was the weight that pulled me down. O
      Cromwell,
The King has gone beyond me. All my glories   490
In that one woman I have lost forever.
No sun shall ever usher forth mine honors,
Or gild again the noble troops that waited
Upon my smiles. Go, get thee from me, Cromwell;
I am a poor fall'n man, unworthy now   495
To be thy lord and master. Seek the King:
That sun, I pray, may never set! I have told him
What and how true thou art. He will advance thee:
Some little memory of me will stir him—
I know his noble nature—not to let   500
Thy hopeful service perish too. Good Cromwell,
Neglect him not: make use now and provide
For thine own future safety.

  Crom.   O my lord,
Must I then leave you? Must I needs forgo   505
So good, so noble, and so true a master?
Bear witness, all that have not hearts of iron,
With what a sorrow Cromwell leaves his lord.
The King shall have my service, but my pray'rs
Forever and forever shall be yours.   510

  Wol. Cromwell, I did not think to shed a tear

541. **naked:** undefended.

In all my miseries, but thou hast forced me;
Out of thy honest truth, to play the woman.
Let's dry our eyes. And thus far hear me, Cromwell;
And, when I am forgotten, as I shall be,   515
And sleep in dull cold marble, where no mention
Of me more must be heard of, say, I taught thee:
Say, Wolsey, that once trod the ways of glory
And sounded all the depths and shoals of honor
Found thee a way, out of his wrack, to rise in;   520
A sure and safe one, though thy master missed it.
Mark but my fall and that that ruined me.
Cromwell, I charge thee, fling away ambition!
By that sin fell the angels. How can man then,
The image of his Maker, hope to win by it?   525
Love thyself last. Cherish those hearts that hate thee:
Corruption wins not more than honesty.
Still in thy right hand carry gentle peace
To silence envious tongues. Be just and fear not.
Let all the ends thou aimst at be thy country's,   530
Thy God's, and truth's. Then if thou fallst, O Crom-
    well,
Thou fallst a blessed martyr! Serve the King.
And prithee, lead me in.
There take an inventory of all I have,   535
To the last penny: 'tis the King's. My robe,
And my integrity to Heaven, is all
I dare now call mine own. O Cromwell, Cromwell!
Had I but served my God with half the zeal
I served my king, He would not in mine age   540
Have left me naked to mine enemies.

Crom. Good sir, have patience.
Wol.   So I have. Farewell
The hopes of Court! My hopes in Heaven do dwell.

                                   Exeunt.

THE FAMOUS HISTORY
OF THE LIFE OF
KING HENRY
THE EIGHTH

ACT IV

IV.i. Anne Bullen passes through the streets in stately procession to her coronation in Westminster Abbey. She entrances the spectators with her beauty and charm. Among the Queen's attendants are Stephen Gardiner, newly created Bishop of Winchester. It is rumored already that Gardiner and Cranmer are unfriendly and that Cromwell, now Master of the Jewel House and a member of the King's Council, sides with Cranmer.

▬▬▬▬▬▬▬▬▬▬▬▬▬▬▬▬

11. **royal minds:** affection for the King.
12. **let 'em have their rights:** give them their due; **forward:** prompt.

The Garter King of Arms. From M. Trentsentsky, *Costumes in Shakespeare's Historical Play of King Henry the Eighth.* (n.d.).

ACT IV

Scene I. [A street in Westminster.]

Enter two Gentlemen, meeting one another.

1. Gent. Y' are well met once again.

2. Gent.   So are you.

1. Gent. You come to take your stand here and behold

The Lady Anne pass from her coronation?   5

2. Gent. 'Tis all my business. At our last encounter

The Duke of Buckingham came from his trial.

1. Gent. 'Tis very true: but that time offered sorrow;

This, general joy.

2. Gent. 'Tis well. The citizens,   10

I am sure, have shown at full their royal minds—

As, let 'em have their rights, they are ever forward—

In celebration of this day with shows,

Pageants, and sights of honor.

1. Gent.   Never greater,   15

Nor, I'll assure you, better taken, sir.

2. Gent. May I be bold to ask what that contains,

35. **cited:** summoned.
37. **main:** unanimous.

That paper in your hand?
    1. Gent.   Yes: 'tis the list
Of those that claim their offices this day   20
By custom of the coronation.
The Duke of Suffolk is the first and claims
To be High Steward; next, the Duke of Norfolk,
He to be Earl Marshal. You may read the rest.
    2. Gent. I thank you, sir. Had I not known those 25
    customs,
I should have been beholding to your paper.
But, I beseech you, what's become of Katharine,
The Princess Dowager? How goes her business?
    1. Gent. That I can tell you too. The Archbishop 30
Of Canterbury, accompanied with other
Learned and reverend fathers of his order,
Held a late court at Dunstable, six miles off
From Ampthill, where the Princess lay, to which
She was often cited by them but appeared not.   35
And, to be short, for not appearance and
The King's late scruple, by the main assent
Of all these learned men she was divorced
And the late marriage made of none effect.
Since which she was removed to Kimbolton,   40
Where she remains now sick.
    2. Gent   Alas, good lady! [*Trumpets.*]
The trumpets sound. Stand close, the Queen is com-
    ing.   *Hautboys.*

SD 44, para. 5 **Garter:** the Garter King of Arms, the principal herald, who, under the Earl Marshal, took part in such formal ceremonies as coronations.

SD 44, para. 6. **Collars of esses:** part of the insignia of the Order of the Garter.

SD 44 para. 8. **Cinque Ports:** Hastings, Sandwich, Dover, Romney, and Hythe. The Cinque Ports Barons' function of carrying the canopy was traditional; **in her hair:** with her hair flowing.

Anne Bullen's coronation procession. From M. Trentsentsky, *Costumes in Shakespeare's Historical Play of King Henry the Eighth.* (n.d.).

THE ORDER OF THE CORONATION

1. *A lively flourish of trumpets.*
2. *Then two Judges.*
3. *Lord Chancellor, with Purse and Mace before him.*
4. *Choristers singing.*   *Music.*
5. *Mayor of London, bearing the Mace. Then Garter, in his coat of arms, and on his head he wore a gilt copper crown.*
6. *Marquess Dorset, bearing a scepter of gold, on his head a demicoronal of gold. With him, the Earl of Surrey, bearing the rod of silver with the dove, crowned with an earl's coronet. Collars of esses.*
7. *Duke of Suffolk, in his robe of estate, his coronet on his head, bearing a long white wand, as High Steward. With him, the Duke of Norfolk, with the rod of marshalship, a coronet on his head. Collars of esses.*
8. *A canopy borne by four of the Cinque Ports; under it, the Queen in her robe; in her hair, richly adorned with pearl, crowned. On each side her, the Bishops of London and Winchester.*
9. *The old Duchess of Norfolk, in a coronal of gold, wrought with flowers, bearing the Queen's train.*
10. *Certain Ladies or Countesses, with plain circlets of gold without flowers.*

Exeunt, first passing over the Stage in Order and State, and then, a great Flourish of Trumpets.

63. happy: fortunate.

2. Gent. A royal train, believe me. These I know.　　45
Who's that that bears the scepter?
1. Gent.　　　　　　　　　　Marquess Dorset.
And that the Earl of Surrey, with the rod.
2. Gent. A bold brave gentleman. That should be
The Duke of Suffolk.　　　　　　　　　　50
1. Gent.　　　　　　'Tis the same: High Steward.
2. Gent. And that my Lord of Norfolk?
1. Gent.　　　　　　　　　　Yes.
2. Gent. [*Looking on the Queen*] Heaven bless thee!
Thou hast the sweetest face I ever looked on.　　55
Sir, as I have a soul, she is an angel.
Our King has all the Indies in his arms,
And more and richer, when he strains that lady.
I cannot blame his conscience.
1. Gent.　　　　　　　　They that bear　　60
The cloth of honor over her are four barons
Of the Cinque Ports.
2. Gent. Those men are happy, and so are all are
　　near her.
I take it, she that carries up the train　　65
Is that old noble lady, Duchess of Norfolk.
1. Gent. It is, and all the rest are countesses.
2. Gent. Their coronets say so. These are stars in-
　　deed,
And sometimes falling ones.　　70
1. Gent.　　　　　　No more of that.
　　　　　　　　　　Exit procession.

72. **broiling:** battling.
76. **rankness:** i.e., offensive odor.
88. **opposing:** exposing.

Enter a third Gentleman.

God save you, sir! Where have you been broiling?
  3. Gent. Among the crowd i' the Abbey, where a
    finger
Could not be wedged in more. I am stifled   75
With the mere rankness of their joy.
  2. Gent.   You saw
The ceremony?
  3. Gent.   That I did.
  1. Gent.   How was it?   80
  3. Gent. Well worth the seeing.
  2. Gent.   Good sir, speak it to us.
  3. Gent. As well as I am able. The rich stream
Of lords and ladies, having brought the Queen
To a prepared place in the choir, fell off   85
A distance from her, while Her Grace sat down
To rest awhile, some half an hour or so,
In a rich chair of state, opposing freely
The beauty of her person to the people.
Believe me, sir, she is the goodliest woman   90
That ever lay by man; which when the people
Had the full view of, such a noise arose
As the shrouds make at sea in a stiff tempest,
As loud and to as many tunes. Hats, cloaks—
Doublets, I think—flew up, and had their faces   95
Been loose, this day they had been lost. Such joy
I never saw before. Great-bellied women,
That had not half a week to go, like rams

99. **press:** throng.

112. **emblems:** symbols.

115. **parted:** departed.

121. **Whitehall:** see I.iii.21.

127. **Stokesley:** John Stokesley, formerly Henry VIII's chaplain and almoner. He was appointed Bishop of London in 1530, probably for his services in polling the Italian humanists about the divorce.

In the old time of war, would shake the press,
And make 'em reel before 'em. No man living   100
Could say, "This is my wife" there, all were woven
So strangely in one piece.

    2. Gent.   But what followed?

    3. Gent. At length Her Grace rose, and with modest
       paces   105
Came to the altar, where she kneeled and saintlike
Cast her fair eyes to Heaven and prayed devoutly;
Then rose again and bowed her to the people;
When by the Archbishop of Canterbury
She had all the royal makings of a queen,   110
As holy oil, Edward Confessor's crown,
The rod, and bird of peace, and all such emblems
Laid nobly on her: which performed, the choir,
With all the choicest music of the kingdom,
Together sung "Te Deum." So she parted,   115
And with the same full state paced back again
To York Place, where the feast is held.

    1. Gent.   Sir,
You must no more call it York Place; that's past:
For, since the Cardinal fell, that title's lost.   120
'Tis now the King's and called Whitehall.

    3. Gent.   I know it;
But 'tis so lately altered that the old name
Is fresh about me.

    2. Gent. What two reverend bishops   125
Were those that went on each side of the Queen?

    3. Gent. Stokesley and Gardiner, the one of Win-
     chester,

129. **preferred:** promoted.

147. **Something I can command:** I can expect some privileges.

Newly preferred from the King's Secretary,
The other, London.   130
    2. Gent. He of Winchester
Is held no great good lover of the Archbishop's,
The virtuous Cranmer.
    3. Gent.   All the land knows that.
However, yet there is no great breach: when it comes, 135
Cranmer will find a friend will not shrink from him.
    2. Gent. Who may that be, I pray you?
    3. Gent.   Thomas Cromwell,
A man in much esteem with the King, and truly
A worthy friend. The King has made him Master   140
O' the Jewel House,
And one, already, of the Privy Council.
    2. Gent. He will deserve more.
    3. Gent.   Yes, without all doubt.
Come, gentlemen, ye shall go my way, which   145
Is to the Court, and there ye shall be my guests.
Something I can command. As I walk thither,
I'll tell ye more.
    Both.   You may command us, sir.
                                     Exeunt.

IV.ii. Katharine, now Princess Dowager, in retirement at Kimbolton Castle, is very ill. Griffith, her gentleman-usher, tells her of the death of Wolsey, soon after his arrest. Katharine comments on the Cardinal's faults, but Griffith defends his learning and generosity and declares that in his fall he made his peace with his own conscience and died happily. As Katharine dozes, she sees a celestial vision foretokening the joys of Heaven that she will soon know. She rouses herself, however, and is indignant when a messenger enters and addresses her as "Grace" instead of "Majesty." The messenger heralds the arrival of Cardinal Capucius, who brings her the King's good wishes in her illness. She bids Capucius deliver to the King a letter she has written concerning their daughter, urging him to be good to her and to find her a worthy husband. She sends Henry her dying blessing by Capucius.

‖‖‖‖‖‖‖‖‖‖‖‖‖‖‖‖‖‖‖‖‖‖‖‖‖

12. **stepped before:** preceded; **happily:** opportunely.

14. **voice:** rumor.

15. **stout:** uncompromising.

17. **tainted:** disgraced.

21. **with easy roads:** by short stages, pausing often.

23. **covent:** company.

Scene II. [An apartment in Kimbolton Castle.]

*Enter Katharine, Dowager, sick, led between Griffith,
her gentleman-usher, and Patience, her woman.*

 Grif. How does your Grace?
 Kath.   O Griffith, sick to death!
My legs, like loaden branches, bow to the earth,
Willing to leave their burden. Reach a chair.
So: now, methinks, I feel a little ease.   5
Didst thou not tell me, Griffith, as thou ledst me,
That the great child of honor, Cardinal Wolsey,
Was dead?
 Grif. Yes, madam, but I think your Grace,
Out of the pain you suffered, gave no ear to't.   10
 Kath. Prithee, good Griffith, tell me how he died.
If well, he stepped before me happily
For my example.
 Grif.   Well, the voice goes, madam:
For after the stout Earl Northumberland   15
Arrested him at York and brought him forward,
As a man sorely tainted, to his answer,
He fell sick suddenly and grew so ill
He could not sit his mule.
 Kath.   Alas, poor man!   20
 Grif. At last, with easy roads, he came to Leicester,
Lodged in the Abbey; where the reverend Abbot,
With all his covent, honorably received him;
To whom he gave these words, "O father Abbot,

28. **eagerly:** sharply.

38. **stomach:** pride.

39. **suggestion:** secret methods.

40. **Simony:** sale of benefices and other ecclesiastical preferments.

44. **pitiful:** merciful.

47. **ill:** sinful; i.e., he was not celibate.

50. **Men's evil manners live in brass:** i.e., the evil that may be said about them is remembered as though engraved on their tombs; a proverbial idea.

An old man, broken with the storms of state,   25
Is come to lay his weary bones among ye:
Give him a little earth for charity!"
So went to bed, where eagerly his sickness
Pursued him still; and three nights after this,
About the hour of eight, which he himself   30
Foretold should be his last, full of repentance,
Continual meditations, tears, and sorrows,
He gave his honors to the world again,
His blessed part to Heaven, and slept in peace.

 Kath. So may he rest: his faults lie gently on him!   35
Yet thus far, Griffith, give me leave to speak him,
And yet with charity. He was a man
Of an unbounded stomach, ever ranking
Himself with princes; one that by suggestion
Tied all the kingdom. Simony was fair play.   40
His own opinion was his law. I' the presence
He would say untruths and be ever double
Both in his words and meaning. He was never,
But where he meant to ruin, pitiful.
His promises were, as he then was, mighty;   45
But his performance, as he is now, nothing.
Of his own body he was ill and gave
The clergy ill example.

 Grif.   Noble madam,
Men's evil manners live in brass; their virtues   50
We write in water. May it please your Highness
To hear me speak his good now?

 Kath.   Yes, good Griffith:

65. **in you:** among you; that is, in England.

66. **Ipswich and Oxford:** both were called Cardinal College; that at Ipswich, Wolsey's birthplace, was dissolved by Henry VIII; the Oxford College was renamed Christ Church and refounded by Henry.

67. **the good that did it:** the virtue that made it.

69. **art:** learning.

I were malicious else.

 Grif.   This Cardinal,   55
Though from an humble stock, undoubtedly
Was fashioned to much honor from his cradle.
He was a scholar, and a ripe and good one;
Exceeding wise, fair-spoken, and persuading;
Lofty and sour to them that loved him not,   60
But to those men that sought him, sweet as summer.
And though he were unsatisfied in getting,
Which was a sin, yet in bestowing, madam,
He was most princely. Ever witness for him
Those twins of learning that he raised in you,   65
Ipswich and Oxford! one of which fell with him,
Unwilling to outlive the good that did it;
The other, though unfinished, yet so famous,
So excellent in art and still so rising,
That Christendom shall ever speak his virtue.   70
His overthrow heaped happiness upon him;
For then, and not till then, he felt himself
And found the blessedness of being little.
And, to add greater honors to his age
Than man could give him, he died fearing God.   75
 Kath. After my death I wish no other herald,
No other speaker of my living actions,
To keep mine honor from corruption,
But such an honest chronicler as Griffith.
Whom I most hated living, thou hast made me,   80
With thy religious truth and modesty,
Now in his ashes honor. Peace be with him!
Patience, be near me still, and set me lower:

SD 90, l. 2. **vizards:** masks; l. 3. **congee:** bow.

I have not long to trouble thee. Good Griffith,
Cause the musicians play me that sad note   85
I named my knell, whilst I sit meditating
On that celestial harmony I go to.

                              Sad and solemn music.
   Grif. She is asleep. Good wench, let's sit down
       quiet,
For fear we wake her. Softly, gentle Patience.   90

The Vision

Enter, solemnly tripping one after another, six Person-
ages, clad in white robes, wearing on their heads gar-
lands of bays, and golden vizards on their faces,
branches of bays or palm in their hands. They first
congee unto her, then dance: and, at certain changes,
the first two hold a spare garland over her head, at
which the other four make reverent curtsies. Then the
two that held the garland deliver the same to the
other next two, who observe the same order in their
changes and holding the garland over her head.
Which done, they deliver the same garland to the last
two: who likewise observe the same order. At which
(as it were by inspiration) she makes (in her sleep)
signs of rejoicing and holdeth up her hands to
Heaven. And so, in their dancing vanish, carrying the
garland with them. The music continues.

   Kath. Spirits of peace, where are ye? Are ye all gone,
And leave me here in wretchedness behind ye?

105. **leave:** cease.
113. **And't like:** if it please.
117. **lose:** let go.
118. **Go to:** come on.

Grif. Madam, we are here.

Kath.   It is not you I call for.
Saw ye none enter since I slept?   95

Grif.   None, madam.

Kath. No? Saw you not even now a blessed troop
Invite me to a banquet, whose bright faces
Cast thousand beams upon me, like the sun?
They promised me eternal happiness   100
And brought me garlands, Griffith, which I feel
I am not worthy yet to wear. I shall, assuredly.

Grif. I am most joyful, madam, such good dreams
Possess your fancy.

Kath.   Bid the music leave;   105
They are harsh and heavy to me.   *Music ceases.*

Pat.   Do you note
How much Her Grace is altered on the sudden?
How long her face is drawn! how pale she looks,
And of an earthy cold! Mark her eyes!   110

Grif. She is going, wench. Pray, pray!

Pat.   Heaven comfort her!

Enter a Messenger.

Mess. And't like your Grace—

Kath.   You are a saucy fellow.
Deserve we no more reverence?   115

Grif.   You are to blame,
Knowing she will not lose her wonted greatness,
To use so rude behavior. Go to, kneel.

Mess. I humbly do entreat your Highness' pardon;

120. **staying:** waiting.
136. **commendations:** greetings.

My haste made me unmannerly. There is staying   120
A gentleman, sent from the King, to see you.
  Kath. Admit him entrance, Griffith. But this fellow
Let me ne'er see again.
                    Exeunt [Griffith] and Messenger.

        Enter [Griffith, with] Capucius.

                    If my sight fail not,
You should be lord ambassador from the Emperor,   125
My royal nephew, and your name Capucius.
  Cap. Madam, the same; your servant.
  Kath.   O my lord,
The times and titles now are altered strangely
With me since first you knew me. But, I pray you,   130
What is your pleasure with me?
  Cap.   Noble lady,
First, mine own service to your Grace; the next,
The King's request that I would visit you;
Who grieves much for your weakness and by me   135
Sends you his princely commendations
And heartily entreats you take good comfort.
  Kath. O my good lord, that comfort comes too late:
'Tis like a pardon after execution.
That gentle physic, given in time, had cured me;   140
But now I am past all comforts here but prayers.
How does His Highness?
  Cap.   Madam, in good health.
  Kath. So may he ever do! and ever flourish
When I shall dwell with worms and my poor name   145

153. **model:** facsimile; personification.
155. **breeding:** upbringing.
166. **honesty:** chastity; **carriage:** conduct.
174. **able:** sufficient.

Banished the kingdom! Patience, is that letter
I caused you write yet sent away?

    Pat. [*Giving it to Katharine*]   No, madam.

    Kath. Sir, I most humbly pray you to deliver
This to my lord the King.   150

    Cap.   Most willing, madam.

    Kath. In which I have commended to his goodness
The model of our chaste loves, his young daughter—
The dews of Heaven fall thick in blessings on her!—
Beseeching him to give her virtuous breeding—   155
She is young and of a noble modest nature:
I hope she will deserve well—and a little
To love her for her mother's sake, that loved him,
Heaven knows how dearly. My next poor petition
Is that His noble Grace would have some pity   160
Upon my wretched women that so long
Have followed both my fortunes faithfully:
Of which there is not one, I dare avow—
And now I should not lie—but will deserve,
For virtue and true beauty of the soul,   165
For honesty and decent carriage,
A right good husband—let him be a noble:
And, sure, those men are happy that shall have 'em.
The last is, for my men—they are the poorest,
But poverty could never draw 'em from me—   170
That they may have their wages duly paid 'em
And something over to remember me by.
If Heaven had pleased to have given me longer life
And able means, we had not parted thus.
These are the whole contents. And, good my lord,   175

181. **fashion:** shape; appearance.

By that you love the dearest in this world,
As you wish Christian peace to souls departed,
Stand these poor people's friend and urge the King
To do me this last right.

   Cap.   By Heaven, I will,   180
Or let me lose the fashion of a man!

   Kath. I thank you, honest lord. Remember me
In all humility unto His Highness:
Say his long trouble now is passing
Out of this world. Tell him in death I blessed him,   185
For so I will. Mine eyes grow dim. Farewell,
My lord. Griffith, farewell. Nay, Patience,
You must not leave me yet. I must to bed:
Call in more women. When I am dead, good wench,
Let me be used with honor. Strew me over   190
With maiden flowers, that all the world may know
I was a chaste wife to my grave. Embalm me,
Then lay me forth; although unqueened, yet like
A queen and daughter to a king inter me.
I can no more.   195

                       Exeunt, leading Katharine.

THE FAMOUS HISTORY
OF THE LIFE OF
KING HENRY
THE EIGHTH

ACT V

V.i. Queen Anne lies in childbed. Gardiner and Sir Thomas Lovell hope for a healthy heir, but Gardiner would be glad if the Queen did not survive. He links her with Cranmer and Cromwell as dangerous to the state of religion in England. Cranmer, already accused to the King of heresy, is to face the Council in the morning. The King, unable longer to distract himself with cards, comes to ask about the Queen's progress. When Cranmer enters in answer to his summons, Henry tells him of the complaints that he must answer before the Council. He gives Cranmer a ring, which he bids him produce if he cannot convince the Councilors of his innocence. The old lady reports that Anne has given birth—to a girl rather than the hoped-for son.

〜〜〜〜〜〜〜〜〜〜〜〜〜〜〜〜

9. **primero:** a card game.

14-5. **And if there be/ No great offense belongs to't:** if there is no great impropriety in doing so.

16. **touch:** hint.

ACT V

~~~~~~

Scene I. [London. A gallery in the Palace.]

*Enter Gardiner, Bishop of Winchester, a Page with a
torch before him, met by Sir Thomas Lovell.*

Gar. It's one o'clock, boy, is't not?
Boy.   It hath struck.
Gar. These should be hours for necessities,
Not for delights; times to repair our nature
With comforting repose and not for us   5
To waste these times. Good hour of night, Sir Thomas!
Whither so late?
Lov.   Came you from the King, my lord?
Gar. I did, Sir Thomas, and left him at primero
With the Duke of Suffolk.   10
Lov.   I must to him too,
Before he go to bed. I'll take my leave.
Gar. Not yet, Sir Thomas Lovell. What's the matter?
It seems you are in haste. And if there be
No great offense belongs to't, give your friend   15
Some touch of your late business. Affairs that walk,
As they say spirits do, at midnight, have

18. **wilder:** more desperate.
19. **dispatch:** settlement.
27. **Good time:** safe arrival.
35. **way:** religious conviction.
41. **remarked:** distinguished.
44. **Stands in the gap and trade of mo pre-ferments:** is in line for other distinguished openings.

In them a wilder nature than the business
That seeks dispatch by day.

    Lov.   My lord, I love you   20
And durst commend a secret to your ear
Much weightier than this work. The Queen's in labor,
They say, in great extremity; and feared
She'll with the labor end.

    Gar.   The fruit she goes with   25
I pray for heartily, that it may find
Good time and live; but for the stock, Sir Thomas,
I wish it grubbed up now.

    Lov.   Methinks I could
Cry the amen; and yet my conscience says   30
She's a good creature, and, sweet lady, does
Deserve our better wishes.

    Gar.   But, sir, sir,
Hear me, Sir Thomas. Y' are a gentleman
Of mine own way: I know you wise, religious;   35
And, let me tell you, it will ne'er be well,
'Twill not, Sir Thomas Lovell, take't of me,
Till Cranmer, Cromwell, her two hands, and she,
Sleep in their graves.

    Lov.   Now, sir, you speak of two   40
The most remarked i' the kingdom. As for Cromwell,
Beside that of the Jewel House, is made Master
O' the Rolls and the King's Secretary; further, sir,
Stands in the gap and trade of mo preferments,
With which the time will load him. The Archbishop   45
Is the King's hand and tongue; and who dare speak

56. **broken with:** broached the subject to.
57. **of:** out of.
58. **fell:** deadly.
59. **reasons:** arguments.
61. **convented:** called.

One syllable against him?
  Gar.   Yes, yes, Sir Thomas,
There are that dare; and I myself have ventured
To speak my mind of him. And indeed this day,   50
Sir, I may tell it you, I think I have
Incensed the lords o' the Council that he is—
For so I know he is, they know he is—
A most arch-heretic, a pestilence
That does infect the land: with which they moved   55
Have broken with the King, who hath so far
Given ear to our complaint, of his great grace
And princely care foreseeing those fell mischiefs
Our reasons laid before him, hath commanded
Tomorrow morning to the Council board   60
He be convented. He's a rank weed, Sir Thomas,
And we must root him out. From your affairs
I hinder you too long. Good night, Sir Thomas.
  Lov. Many good nights, my lord. I rest your servant.
                 Exeunt Gardiner and Page.

Enter King and Suffolk.

  King. Charles, I will play no more tonight;   65
My mind's not on't. You are too hard for me.
  Suf. Sir, I did never win of you before.
  King. But little, Charles,
Nor shall not, when my fancy's on my play.
Now, Lovell, from the Queen what is the news?   70
  Lov. I could not personally deliver to her
What you commanded me, but by her woman

78. **suff'rance:** suffering.
82. **quit:** deliver.
87. **estate:** condition.

I sent your message; who returned her thanks
In the great'st humbleness and desired your Highness
Most heartily to pray for her.   75
    King.   What sayst thou, ha?
To pray for her? What, is she crying out?
    Lov. So said her woman, and that her suff'rance made
Almost each pang a death.   80
    King.   Alas, good lady!
    Suf. God safely quit her of her burden and
With gentle travail, to the gladding of
Your Highness with an heir!
    King.   'Tis midnight, Charles.   85
Prithee, to bed and in thy pray'rs remember
The estate of my poor queen. Leave me alone,
For I must think of that which company
Would not be friendly to.
    Suf.   I wish your Highness   90
A quiet night, and my good mistress will
Remember in my prayers.
    King.   Charles, good night.
                             Exit Suffolk.

          Enter Sir Anthony Denny.

Well, sir, what follows?
    Den. Sir, I have brought my lord the Archbishop,   95
As you commanded me.
    King.   Ha! Canterbury?

104. **happily:** opportunely.
105. **Avoid:** vacate.

Thomas Cranmer's dress as Archbishop of Canterbury. From M. Trentsentsky, *Costumes in Shakespeare's Historical Play of King Henry the Eighth*. (n.d.).

Den. Ay, my good lord,

King.   'Tis true: where is he, Denny?

Den. He attends your Highness' pleasure.   100

King.   Bring him to us.

[*Exit Denny.*]

Lov. [*Aside*] This is about that which the Bishop
   spake:

I am happily come hither.

Enter Cranmer and Denny.

King. Avoid the gallery. (*Lovell seems to stay.*) Ha! 105
   I have said. Be gone!

What!   *Exeunt Lovell and Denny.*

Cran. [*Aside*] I am fearful. Wherefore frowns he
   thus?

'Tis his aspect of terror. All's not well.   110

King. How now, my lord! you do desire to know

Wherefore I sent for you.

Cran. [*Kneeling*]   It is my duty

T' attend your Highness' pleasure.

King.   Pray you, arise,   115

My good and gracious Lord of Canterbury.

Come, you and I must walk a turn together:

I have news to tell you. Come, come, give me your
   hand.

Ah, my good lord, I grieve at what I speak   120

And am right sorry to repeat what follows.

I have, and most unwillingly, of late

Heard many grievous, I do say, my lord,

131. **You a brother of us:** you being as dear to me as a brother.

132. **fits:** is becoming.

136. **throughly:** thoroughly; **winnowed:** sifted.

138. **stands under:** is subject to.

143. **holidame:** originally "halidom," literally, "holy relic," later misinterpreted as referring to the Virgin.

144. **looked:** expected.

148. **indurance:** imprisonment.

150. **stand:** rely.

152. **weigh:** value.

153. **Being of those virtues vacant:** being emptied of those virtues.

Grievous, complaints of you, which, being considered,
Have moved us and our council that you shall   125
This morning come before us, where, I know,
You cannot with such freedom purge yourself
But that, till further trial in those charges
Which will require your answer, you must take
Your patience to you and be well contented   130
To make your house our Tow'r. You a brother of us,
It fits we thus proceed, or else no witness
Would come against you.

   Cran. [*Kneeling*]   I humbly thank your Highness
And am right glad to catch this good occasion   135
Most throughly to be winnowed, where my chaff
And corn shall fly asunder: for, I know,
There's none stands under more calumnious tongues
Than I myself, poor man.

   King.   Stand up, good Canterbury.   140
Thy truth and thy integrity is rooted
In us, thy friend. Give me thy hand, stand up.
Prithee, let's walk. Now, by my holidame,
What manner of man are you? My lord, I looked
You would have given me your petition that   145
I should have ta'en some pains to bring together
Yourself and your accusers and to have heard you,
Without indurance further.

   Cran.   Most dread liege,
The good I stand on is my truth and honesty.   150
If they shall fail, I, with mine enemies,
Will triumph o'er my person, which I weigh not,
Being of those virtues vacant. I fear nothing

161. **due:** award; **At what ease:** how easily.
165. **Ween you of:** do you count on.
168. **naughty:** wicked.
169. **leap of danger:** dangerous leap.

What can be said against me.

 King.   Know you not   155
How your state stands i' the world, with the whole
 world?
Your enemies are many and not small; their practices
Must bear the same proportion; and not ever
The justice and the truth o' the question carries 160
The due o' the verdict with it. At what ease
Might corrupt minds procure knaves as corrupt
To swear against you? Such things have been done.
You are potently opposed and with a malice
Of as great size. Ween you of better luck, 165
I mean, in perjured witness, than your master,
Whose minister you are, whiles here He lived
Upon this naughty earth? Go to, go to:
You take a precipice for no leap of danger
And woo your own destruction.   170

 Cran.   God and your Majesty
Protect mine innocence, or I fall into
The trap is laid for me!

 King.   Be of good cheer:
They shall no more prevail than we give way to. 175
Keep comfort to you, and this morning see
You do appear before them. If they shall chance,
In charging you with matters, to commit you,
The best persuasions to the contrary
Fail not to use, and with what vehemency 180
The occasion shall instruct you. If entreaties
Will render you no remedy, this ring
Deliver them and your appeal to us

194. shade: shadow; protect.

There make before them. Look, the good man weeps!
He's honest, on mine honor. God's blest mother!   185
I swear he is true-hearted and a soul
None better in my kingdom. Get you gone,
And do as I have bid you. (*Exit Cranmer.*) He has strangled
His language in his tears.   190

Enter Old Lady, [Lovell following].

  Gent. (Within)   Come back: what mean you?
  Old La. I'll not come back: the tidings that I bring
Will make my boldness manners. Now, good angels
Fly o'er thy royal head and shade thy person
Under their blessed wings!   195
  King.   Now, by thy looks
I guess thy message. Is the Queen delivered?
Say, ay, and of a boy.
  Old La.   Ay, ay, my liege;
And of a lovely boy: the God of Heaven   200
Both now and ever bless her! 'Tis a girl,
Promises boys hereafter. Sir, your queen
Desires your visitation, and to be
Acquainted with this stranger: 'tis as like you
As cherry is to cherry.   205
  King.   Lovell!
  Lov.   Sir?
  King. Give her an hundred marks. I'll to the Queen.
                              Exit King.

209. **By this light:** a common oath.
215. **put it to the issue:** force it to a conclusion.

||||||||||||||||||||||||||||||||||||||||||||||||||||||||||

V.ii. Cranmer arrives at the Council chamber and is made to wait outside until the Council is pleased to see him. Dr. Butts, noting this discourtesy, hurries off to inform the King.

||||||||||||||||||||||||||||||||||||||||

4. **All fast:** all the doors secured.
5. **waits:** attends.

Old La. An hundred marks! By this light, I'll ha'
    more.   210
An ordinary groom is for such payment.
I will have more, or scold it out of him.
Said I for this the girl was like to him?
I'll have more, or else unsay't; and now,
While 'tis hot, I'll put it to the issue.   215

                            Exeunt.

Scene II. [London. Before the Council chamber.]

Pursuivants, Pages, and others attending.
Enter Cranmer, Archbishop of Canterbury.

Cran. I hope I am not too late; and yet the gentle-
    man
That was sent to me from the Council prayed me
To make great haste. All fast? What means this? Ho!
Who waits there? Sure, you know me?   5

Enter Keeper.

Keep.   Yes, my lord;
But yet I cannot help you.
    Cran. Why?
    Keep. Your Grace must wait till you be called for.

13. **understand it presently:** know it immediately.

17. **sound:** perceive.

Enter Doctor Butts.

Cran.   So.   10
  Butts. [*Aside*] This is a piece of malice. I am glad
I came this way so happily: the King
Shall understand it presently.   *Exit.*
  Cran. [*Aside*]   'Tis Butts,
The King's physician. As he passed along,   15
How earnestly he cast his eyes upon me!
Pray Heaven, he sound not my disgrace! For certain,
This is of purpose laid by some that hate me—
God turn their hearts! I never sought their malice—
To quench mine honor. They would shame to make   20
    me
Wait else at door, a fellow Councilor,
'Mong boys, grooms, and lackeys. But their pleasures
Must be fulfilled, and I attend with patience.

Enter the King and Butts at a window above.

  Butts. I'll show your Grace the strangest sight—   25
  King.   What's that, Butts?
  Butts. I think your Highness saw this many a day.
  King. Body o 'me, where is it?
  Butts.   There, my lord:
The high promotion of His Grace of Canterbury;   30
Who holds his state at door, 'mongst pursuivants,
Pages, and footboys.
  King.   Ha! 'tis he, indeed.

36. **parted:** shared.
37. **suffer:** permit.
40. **post:** messenger.

‖‖

V.[iii.] The Lord Chancellor accuses Cranmer on behalf of the Council of spreading new and dangerous opinions about religion. Cranmer asks that his accusers be brought before him so that he can answer them directly. He is told that, because he is a Councilor, no one dares accuse him. The King, he is also told, ordered him committed to the Tower of London while the Council considers charges against him. Seeing no other way to avoid the Tower, Cranmer produces the King's ring. Immediately afterward the King himself enters, defends Cranmer, and expresses his displeasure at the Councilors' treatment of him. Turning to Cranmer, he requests him to be godfather at the christening of his newborn daughter.

Is this the honor they do one another?
'Tis well there's one above 'em yet. I had thought   35
They had parted so much honesty among 'em,
At least good manners, as not thus to suffer
A man of his place and so near our favor
To dance attendance on Their Lordships' pleasures,
And at the door too, like a post with packets.   40
By holy Mary, Butts, there's knavery!
Let 'em alone and draw the curtain close:
We shall hear more anon.

                                        [*Exeunt.*]

[Scene III. The Council chamber.]

A council table brought in, with chairs and stools, and
placed under the state. Enter Lord Chancellor, places
himself at the upper end of the table on the left hand,
a seat being left void above him, as for Canterbury's
seat. Duke of Suffolk, Duke of Norfolk, Surrey, Lord
Chamberlain, Gardiner, seat themselves in order on
each side. Cromwell at lower end, as Secretary.
                [Keeper at the door.]

  Chan. Speak to the business, Master Secretary:
Why are we met in council?
  Crom.   Please your Honors,
The chief cause concerns His Grace of Canterbury.
  Gar. Has he had knowledge of it?   5

17-8. **capable/ Of our flesh:** susceptible to human weakness; imperfect.
25. **Divers:** different; unusual.
29. **Pace 'em:** put them through their paces.
30. **stubborn:** fierce.
31. **manage:** handling.

Crom.   Yes.
Nor.   Who waits there?
Keep. Without, my noble lords?
Gar.   Yes.
Keep.   My Lord Archbishop;   10
And has done half an hour, to know your pleasures.
Chan. Let him come in.
Keep.   Your Grace may enter now.

Cranmer [enters and] approaches the council table.

Chan. My good Lord Archbishop, I'm very sorry
To sit here at this present and behold   15
That chair stand empty: but we all are men,
In our own natures frail, and capable
Of our flesh; few are angels: out of which frailty
And want of wisdom, you, that best should teach us,
Have misdemeaned yourself, and not a little,   20
Toward the King first, then his laws, in filling
The whole realm, by your teaching and your chap-
    lains—
For so we are informed—with new opinions,
Divers and dangerous, which are heresies,   25
And, not reformed, may prove pernicious.
Gar. Which reformation must be sudden too,
My noble lords; for those that tame wild horses
Pace 'em not in their hands to make 'em gentle,
But stop their mouths with stubborn bits and spur 'em   30
Till they obey the manage. If we suffer,

32. **easiness:** laxness.
35. **taint:** infection.
37. **dearly:** earnestly; sorrowfully.
41. **study:** effort.
45. **single:** sincere.
51. **crooked:** adverse.
55. **urge:** plead.

Out of our easiness and childish pity
To one man's honor, this contagious sickness,
Farewell all physic. And what follows then?
Commotions, uproars, with a general taint   35
Of the whole state; as of late days our neighbors,
The upper Germany, can dearly witness,
Yet freshly pitied in our memories.

   Cran. My good lords, hitherto, in all the progress
Both of my life and office, I have labored,   40
And with no little study, that my teaching
And the strong course of my authority
Might go one way and safely; and the end
Was ever to do well: nor is there living,
I speak it with a single heart, my lords,   45
A man that more detests, more stirs against,
Both in his private conscience and his place,
Defacers of a public peace, than I do.
Pray Heaven the King may never find a heart
With less allegiance in it! Men that make   50
Envy and crooked malice nourishment
Dare bite the best. I do beseech your Lordships
That, in this case of justice, my accusers,
Be what they will, may stand forth face to face
And freely urge against me.   55
   Suf.   Nay, my lord,
That cannot be. You are a Councilor,
And, by that virtue, no man dare accuse you.
   Gar. My lord, because we have business of more
     moment,   60

75. **modesty:** moderation.

77. **Lay all the weight you can upon my patience:** no matter how heavily you press me.

81. **sectary:** an advocate of a sect; i.e., Lutheranism.

82. **painted gloss:** dissimulation; **discovers:** reveals.

83. **words and weakness:** insubstantial words.

85. **By your good favor:** if you will pardon my saying so.

90. **cry your Honor mercy:** beg your Honor's pardon.

We will be short with you. 'Tis His Highness'
    pleasure,
And our consent, for better trial of you,
From hence you be committed to the Tower;
Where, being but a private man again,   65
You shall know many dare accuse you boldly,
More than, I fear, you are provided for.
    Cran. Ah, my good Lord of Winchester, I thank
    you.
You are always my good friend: if your will pass,   70
I shall both find your Lordship judge and juror,
You are so merciful. I see your end:
'Tis my undoing. Love and meekness, lord,
Become a churchman better than ambition;
Win straying souls with modesty again,   75
Cast none away. That I shall clear myself,
Lay all the weight ye can upon my patience,
I make as little doubt as you do conscience
In doing daily wrongs. I could say more,
But reverence to your calling makes me modest.   80
    Gar. My lord, my lord, you are a sectary;
That's the plain truth. Your painted gloss discovers,
To men that understand you, words and weakness.
    Crom. My Lord of Winchester, y' are a little,
By your good favor, too sharp: men so noble,   85
However faulty, yet should find respect
For what they have been. 'Tis a cruelty
To load a falling man.
    Gar.   Good Master Secretary,
I cry your Honor mercy: you may, worst   90

94. **sound:** faithful (to established religious tenets).

Of all this table, say so.

    Crom.   Why, my lord?

    Gar. Do not I know you for a favorer

Of this new sect? Ye are not sound.

    Crom.   Not sound?   95

    Gar. Not sound, I say.

    Crom.   Would you were half so honest!

Men's prayers then would seek you, not their fears.

    Gar. I shall remember this bold language.

    Crom.   Do.   100

Remember your bold life too.

    Chan.   This is too much:

Forbear, for shame, my lords.

    Gar.   I have done.

    Crom.   And I.   105

    Chan. Then thus for you, my lord: it stands agreed,

I take it, by all voices, that forthwith

You be conveyed to the Tower a prisoner;

There to remain till the King's further pleasure

Be known unto us. Are you all agreed, lords?   110

    All. We are.

    Cram.   Is there no other way of mercy,

But I must needs to the Tower, my lords?

    Gar.   What other

Would you expect? You are strangely troublesome.   115

Let some o' the guard be ready there.

124. **gripes:** grasps.
128. **right:** true.
132. **but:** even.
137. **My mind gave me:** I suspected.
140. **envy at:** feel hostile toward.
141. **have at ye:** protect yourselves.

Enter the Guard.

Cran.   For me?
Must I go like a traitor thither?
  Gar.   Receive him,
And see him safe i' the Tower.   120
  Cran.   Stay, good my lords,
I have a little yet to say. Look there, my lords;
By virtue of that ring, I take my cause
Out of the gripes of cruel men, and give it
To a most noble judge, the King my master.   125
  Cham. This is the King's ring.
  Sur.   'Tis no counterfeit.
  Suf. 'Tis the right ring, by Heaven. I told ye all,
When we first put this dangerous stone arolling,
'Twould fall upon ourselves.   130
  Nor.   Do you think, my lords,
The King will suffer but the little finger
Of this man to be vexed?
  Cham.   -   'Tis now too certain.
How much more is his life in value with him?   135
Would I were fairly out on't!
  Crom.   My mind gave me,
In seeking tales and informations
Against this man, whose honesty the Devil
And his disciples only envy at,   140
Ye blew the fire that burns ye: now have at ye!

148. dear: devoted.

Enter King, frowning on them, [and] takes his seat.

  Gar. Dread sovereign, how much are we bound to
    Heaven
In daily thanks that gave us such a prince,
Not only good and wise but most religious: 145
One that, in all obedience, makes the Church
The chief aim of his honor; and, to strengthen
That holy duty, out of dear respect,
His royal self in judgment comes to hear
The cause betwixt her and this great offender.   150
  King. You were ever good at sudden commenda-
    tions,
Bishop of Winchester. But know, I come not
To hear such flattery now, and in my presence
They are too thin and bare to hide offenses.   155
To me you cannot reach. You play the spaniel,
And think with wagging of your tongue to win me;
But, whatsoe'er thou takest me for, I'm sure
Thou hast a cruel nature and a bloody.
[*To Cranmer*] Good man, sit down. Now let me see 160
    the proudest
He that dares most but wag his finger at thee.
By all that's holy, he had better starve
Than but once think this place becomes thee not.
  Sur. May it please your Grace—   165
  King.   No, sir, it does not please me.
I had thought I had had men of some understanding
And wisdom of my Council; but I find none.

178. **mean:** opportunity.
181. **like:** please.
186. **in me:** so far as I am concerned.
196. **wants:** lacks.

Was it discretion, lords, to let this man,
This good man—few of you deserve that title—   170
This honest man, wait like a lousy footboy
At chamber door? and one as great as you are?
Why, what a shame was this! Did my commission
Bid ye so far forget yourselves? I gave ye
Power as he was a Councilor to try him,   175
Not as a groom. There's some of ye, I see,
More out of malice than integrity,
Would try him to the utmost, had ye mean;
Which ye shall never have while I live.

  Chan.   Thus far,   180
My most dread sovereign, may it like your Grace
To let my tongue excuse all. What was purposed
Concerning his imprisonment was rather,
If there be faith in men, meant for his trial
And fair purgation to the world than malice,   185
I'm sure, in me.

  King.   Well, well, my lords, respect him;
Take him and use him well; he's worthy of it.
I will say thus much for him: if a prince
May be beholding to a subject, I   190
Am for his love and service so to him.
Make me no more ado, but all embrace him.
Be friends, for shame, my lords! My Lord of Canter-
    bury,
I have a suit which you must not deny me;   195
That is, a fair young maid that yet wants baptism;
You must be godfather and answer for her.

  Cran. The greatest monarch now alive may glory

201-2. **spare your spoons:** save the spoons traditionally given to the newly-christened child.

215. **shrewd:** malicious.

218. **made ye one:** reconciled you.

||||||||||||||||||||||||||||||||||||||||||||||||||||||||||

V.[iv.] A great crowd has gathered outside the palace to see the procession for the Princess' christening.

||||||||||||||||||||||||||||||||||||||||

2. **Parish Garden:** Paris Garden, a manor on the Southwark side of the Thames, site of an arena where bears and bulls were baited.

In such an honor. How may I deserve it,
That am a poor and humble subject to you? 200

 King. Come, come, my lord, you'd spare your
spoons. You shall have two noble partners with you,
the old Duchess of Norfolk and Lady Marquess
Dorset. Will these please you?
Once more, my Lord of Winchester, I charge you, 205
Embrace and love this man.

 Gar.   With a true heart
And brother love I do it.

 Cran.   And let Heaven
Witness how dear I hold this confirmation. 210

 King. Good man, those joyful tears show thy true
  heart.
The common voice, I see, is verified
Of thee, which says thus: "Do my Lord of Canterbury
A shrewd turn and he's your friend forever." 215
Come, lords, we trifle time away. I long
To have this young one made a Christian.
As I have made ye one, lords, one remain;
So I grow stronger, you more honor gain.

            Exeunt.

Scene [IV. London. The Palace yard.]

Noise and tumult within. Enter Porter and his Man.

 Port. You'll leave your noise anon, ye rascals. Do
you take the court for Parish Garden? Ye rude slaves,
leave your gaping.

6. **to:** in comparison with.

16. **Powle's:** St. Paul's Cathedral.

21. **made no spare:** spared no effort.

23. **Sir Guy:** Guy of Warwick, a hero in a popular romantic tale; **Colbrand:** a giant slain by Guy of Warwick.

26. **cuckold:** betrayed husband.

27. **chine:** side of beef.

28. **for a cow:** a common saying of imprecise meaning.

([*Voice*] *Within.*) Good Master Porter, I belong to
   the larder.   5

Port. Belong to the gallows and be hanged, ye
rogue! Is this a place to roar in? Fetch me a dozen
crab tree staves, and strong ones: these are but
switches to 'em. I'll scratch your heads. You must
be seeing christenings? Do you look for ale and cakes   10
here, you rude rascals?

Man. Pray, sir, be patient. 'Tis as much impossible—
Unless we sweep 'em from the door with cannons—
To scatter 'em as 'tis to make 'em sleep
On May Day morning, which will never be.   15
We may as well push against Powle's as stir 'em.

Port. How got they in, and be hanged?

Man. Alas, I know not: how gets the tide in?
As much as one sound cudgel of four foot—
You see the poor remainder—could distribute,   20
I made no spare, sir.

Port.   You did nothing, sir.

Man. I am not Samson, nor Sir Guy, nor Colbrand,
To mow 'em down before me. But if I spared any
That had a head to hit, either young or old,   25
He or she, cuckold or cuckold-maker,
Let me ne'er hope to see a chine again;
And that I would not for a cow, God save her!

([*Voice*] *Within*). Do you hear, Master Porter?

Port. I shall be with you presently, good Master   30
Puppy. Keep the door closed, sirrah.

Man. What would you have me do?

Port. What should you do, but knock 'em down by

34. **Moorfields:** an open field outside the city walls to the North, used as a recreation ground.

37. **fry:** spawn; brood.

43. **brazier:** (1) worker in brass; (2) utensil for burning coals.

45. **under the line:** below the equator; i.e., in a torrid zone.

46. **firedrake:** (1) furnace tender; (2) meteor.

50-1. **railed upon me:** scolded me.

51. **pinked porringer:** a small, round hat, shaped like a porridge dish, with perforated decoration.

54. **Clubs:** an appeal to men armed with clubs to defend her. Clubs were usually the weapon of apprentices, who were always willing to join a fray.

56. **Strond:** Strand; **made good:** defended.

58-9. **came to the broomstaff to me:** began fighting with me hand to hand.

60. **loose shot:** independent marksmen.

61. **fain:** forced.

62. **work:** fort.

the dozens? Is this Moorfields to muster in? Or
have we some strange Indian with the great tool   35
come to Court, the women so besiege us? Bless
me, what a fry of fornication is at door! On my
Christian conscience, this one christening will beget
a thousand: here will be father, godfather, and all
together.   40

Man. The spoons will be the bigger, sir. There is a
fellow somewhat near the door, he should be a
brazier by his face, for, o' my conscience, twenty
of the dog days now reign in 's nose. All that
stand about him are under the line, they need   45
no other penance. That firedrake did I hit three
times on the head, and three times was his nose
discharged against me. He stands there, like a
mortar piece, to blow us. There was a haber-
dasher's wife of small wit near him, that railed   50
upon me till her pinked porringer fell off her
head, for kindling such a combustion in the state.
I missed the meteor once and hit that woman,
who cried out, "Clubs!" when I might see from
far some forty truncheoners draw to her succor,   55
which were the hope o' the Strond, where she
was quartered. They fell on: I made good my
place. At length they came to the broomstaff to
me; I defied 'em still: when suddenly a file of
boys behind 'em, loose shot, delivered such a   60
show'r of pebbles that I was fain to draw mine
honor in and let 'em win the work. The Devil was
amongst 'em, I think, surely.

66. **tribulation:** troublesome tribe.

66. **of Tower Hill:** i.e., such as watched executions at the Tower.

67. **limbs:** offspring; **Limehouse:** then, as now, a rough district.

68. **Limbo Patrum:** i.e., prison.

70. **beadles:** officials who administered beatings.

75. **Y' have made a fine hand:** you have done a fine job; a common phrase.

76. **trim:** splendid.

77. **the suburbs:** being outside of the City's jurisdiction, the suburbs were haunted by rogues and harlots.

85-6. **lay ye all/ By the heels:** put you all in the stocks, or in fetters.

87. **round:** large.

88. **baiting of bombards:** swigging from bottles; perhaps with a pun on "bating," "lessening."

Port. These are the youths that thunder at a playhouse and fight for bitten apples; that no audi-   65
ence but the tribulation of Tower Hill or the
limbs of Limehouse, their dear brothers, are able
to endure. I have some of 'em in Limbo Patrum,
and there they are like to dance these three days;
besides the running banquet of two beadles that   70
is to come.

Enter Lord Chamberlain.

Cham. Mercy o' me, what a multitude are here!
They grow still too; from all parts they are coming,
As if we kept a fair here. Where are these porters,
These lazy knaves? Y' have made a fine hand, fellows!   75
There's a trim rabble let in. Are all these
Your faithful friends o' the suburbs? We shall have
Great store of room, no doubt, left for the ladies,
When they pass back from the christening!
Port.   And't please your Honor,   80
We are but men; and what so many may do,
Not being torn a-pieces, we have done.
An army cannot rule 'em.
Cham.   As I live,
If the King blame me for't, I'll lay ye all   85
By the heels, and suddenly; and on your heads
Clap round fines for neglect. Y' are lazy knaves;
And here ye lie baiting of bombards when
Ye should do service. Hark! the trumpets sound;
Th' are come already from the christening.   90

93. **Marshalsea:** a London prison; **hold ye play:** i.e., keep you occupied.

97. **camlet:** a fabric, originally an expensive one from the East, but later made of less costly fibers.

98. **peck:** pitch; **pale:** fence.

‖‖

V.[v.] As he christens the infant Princess Elizabeth, Cranmer prophesies that she will be a blessing to her kingdom and be followed by another ruler who will be equally admired.

Go, break among the press and find a way out
To let the troop pass fairly, or I'll find
A Marshalsea shall hold ye play these two months.
   Port. Make way there for the Princess.
   Man.   You great fellow,   95
Stand close up, or I'll make your head ache.
   Port. You i' the camlet, get up o' the rail:
I'll peck you o'er the pales else.

                          Exeunt.

Scene [V. London. The Palace.]

*Enter Trumpets, sounding: then two Aldermen, Lord
Mayor, Garter, Cranmer, Duke of Norfolk with his
Marshal's staff, Duke of Suffolk, two Noblemen bearing great standing bowls for the christening gifts: then
four Noblemen bearing a canopy, under which the
Duchess of Norfolk, godmother, bearing the child richly habited in a mantle, etc., train borne by a Lady;
then follows the Marchioness Dorset, the other godmother, and Ladies. The troop pass once about the
stage and Garter speaks.*

   Gar. Heaven, from thy endless goodness, send prosperous life, long and ever happy, to the high and
mighty Princess of England, Elizabeth!

7. **gracious:** graced.

11. **What is her name:** a ritual question, not indicating ignorance of the matter.

17. **gossips:** godparents.

23. **Heaven still move about her:** may Heaven ever attend her.

29. **succeed:** follow; **Saba:** the Queen of Sheba.

The Lord Mayor of London. From M. Trentsentsky, *Costumes in Shakespeare's Historical Play of King Henry the Eighth.* (n.d.).

Flourish. Enter King and Guard.

 Cran. [*Kneeling*] And to your royal Grace and the
  good Queen,   5
My noble partners and myself thus pray
All comfort, joy, in this most gracious lady
Heaven ever laid up to make parents happy,
May hourly fall upon ye!
 King.   Thank you, good Lord Archbishop: 10
What is her name?
 Cran.   Elizabeth.
 King.   Stand up, lord.
    [*The King kisses the child.*]
With this kiss take my blessing. God protect thee!
Into whose hand I give thy life.   15
 Cran.   Amen.
 King. My noble gossips, y' have been too prodigal:
I thank ye heartily; so shall this lady,
When she has so much English.
 Cran.   Let me speak, sir, 20
For Heaven now bids me; and the words I utter
Let none think flattery, for they'll find 'em truth.
This royal infant—Heaven still move about her!—
Though in her cradle, yet now promises
Upon this land a thousand, thousand blessings, 25
Which time shall bring to ripeness. She shall be—
But few now living can behold that goodness—
A pattern to all princes living with her
And all that shall succeed. Saba was never

47. **sleep:** i.e., die.

48. **phoenix:** fabulous bird that consumed itself on a funeral pyre at a vast age, another phoenix rising from the ashes.

49. **heir:** James I, who came to the throne on Elizabeth's death in 1603.

50. **admiration:** admirable qualities.

The phoenix reborn from its funeral pyre. From Geoffrey Whitney, *A Choice of Emblems* (1586).

More covetous of wisdom and fair virtue   30
Than this pure soul shall be. All princely graces
That mold up such a mighty piece as this is,
With all the virtues that attend the good,
Shall still be doubled on her. Truth shall nurse her,
Holy and heavenly thoughts still counsel her.   35
She shall be loved and feared. Her own shall bless
    her;
Her foes shake like a field of beaten corn
And hang their heads with sorrow. Good grows with
    her.   40
In her days every man shall eat in safety
Under his own vine what he plants and sing
The merry songs of peace to all his neighbors.
God shall be truly known; and those about her
From her shall read the perfect ways of honor,   45
And by those claim their greatness, not by blood.
Nor shall this peace sleep with her, but, as when
The bird of wonder dies, the maiden phoenix,
Her ashes new create another heir
As great in admiration as herself,   50
So shall she leave her blessedness to one—
When Heaven shall call her from this cloud of dark-
    ness—
Who from the sacred ashes of her honor
Shall starlike rise, as great in fame as she was,   55
And so stand fixed. Peace, plenty, love, truth, terror,
That were the servants to this chosen infant,
Shall then be his and like a vine grow to him.
Wherever the bright sun of Heaven shall shine

75. get: beget.

His honor and the greatness of his name   60
Shall be and make new nations. He shall flourish
And, like a mountain cedar, reach his branches
To all the plains about him. Our children's children
Shall see this and bless Heaven.

   King.   Thou speakest wonders.   65
   Cran. She shall be, to the happiness of England,
An aged princess: many days shall see her,
And yet no day without a deed to crown it.
Would I had known no more! But she must die;
She must; the saints must have her; yet a virgin,   70
A most unspotted lily shall she pass
To the ground, and all the world shall mourn her.

   King. O Lord Archbishop,
Thou hast made me now a man! Never before
This happy child did I get anything.   75
This oracle of comfort has so pleased me
That when I am in Heaven I shall desire
To see what this child does and praise my Maker.
I thank ye all. To you, my good Lord Mayor,
And you, good brethren, I am much beholding;   80
I have received much honor by your presence,
And ye shall find me thankful. Lead the way, lords:
Ye must all see the Queen, and she must thank ye:
She will be sick else. This day, no man think
Has business at his house; for all shall stay: 85
This little one shall make it holiday.

                                    Exeunt.

Epil. The Chorus, begging the audience's indulgence for the play just witnessed, counts on the applause of virtuous women, who should be pleased at the one portrayed in the drama. And, surely, if women applaud the performance, men will not dare to withhold their own approval.

⸻⸻⸻⸻⸻

8. **expected good:** hoped-for reward; **like:** likely.
13. **ill hap:** back luck (for them).